IMPORTANT NEWS
In June 1991 Lynn Farrell discovered one
plant of Early Soider Orchid in TL78, West
Suffolk.
This exciting find is the first Suffolk record
for over 200 years and the first north of the
River Thames for a very long time. It must
have arisen from wind-blown seed and have
benefitted from recent warm summers.

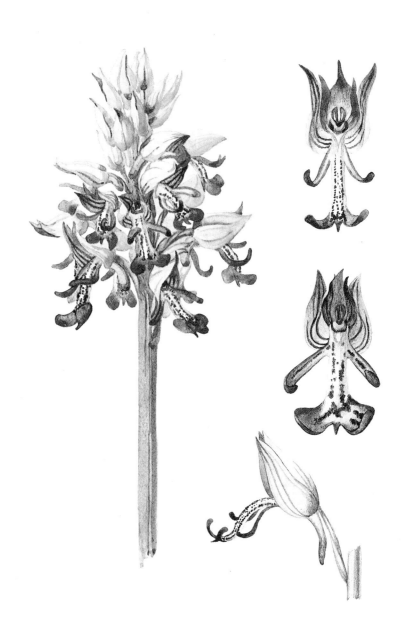

Military Orchid *Orchis militaris*, May, 1957. An original watercolour by Olive Milne-Redhead

THE
ORCHIDS
OF
SUFFOLK
AN ATLAS & HISTORY

Martin Sanford

SUFFOLK NATURALISTS' SOCIETY

Published by The Suffolk Naturalists' Society, c/o The Museum, High Street, Ipswich, IP1 3QH

ISBN 0-9508154-3-8

Typeset in Plantin
Printed by: Ancient House Printing Group, Hadleigh Road Industrial Estate, Ipswich.

Front cover – Southern Marsh Orchids at Melton Mead. (R. Dryden)

CONTENTS

To my daughter, Jasmine Lily.

FOREWORD

I am delighted and honoured to be asked to write the foreword to this splendid account of Suffolk Orchids, past and present.

My own interest in British Orchids dates back to my childhood days. In the garden of our home in east Somerset, there were Green-winged, Lady's-tresses and Bee Orchids growing on the lawns and Broad-leaved Helleborine in the shrubbery. Early-purple Orchid was in a nearby hedgerow and, in a local wood, Greater Butterfly Orchid flourished. I was thrilled when I found a plant of the Bird's-nest Orchid in another neighbouring wood and the Early Marsh-orchid in my father's field (usually grazed), the one year it was set for hay.

Then, as a teenager, living in Cheltenham, I became familiar with Fragrant, Common Spotted, Musk, Frog, the Pyramidal and the Burnt Orchids in Cotswold grasslands whilst, in the woods, the Fly Orchid and the White Helleborine were frequently encountered.

More recently, I was privileged to see the Lizard Orchid in Bedfordshire, the Red Helleborine in the Cotswolds, the Ghost Orchid in the Chilterns and, last but not least, the Military Orchid in Suffolk. I was lucky to have been able to study populations of Marsh and Spotted Orchids in various parts of Britain with my friend and colleague at Kew, Victor Summerhayes, while he was collecting data for his New Naturalist book. On one occasion, I visited with him the remarkable site near Southampton where five species of these orchids grew together and, of course, hybridised – a unique site since destroyed by a motorway.

In the 1950s, I helped organise the first scrub-clearing operation in Britain to save a rare species, the Monkey Orchid, in its Oxfordshire site, some years before the British Trust for Conservation Volunteers was formed to carry out such activities. I have also taken an active part in trying to save the Lady's Slipper Orchid from extinction in Britain.

This historic account of Suffolk Orchids brings home the vast extent of habitat loss that has occurred since the last century, and which, in spite of scheduling of Sites of Special Scientific Interest, is continuing today, as many SSSIs are being damaged or destroyed by roadworks or developments. Suffolk has lost most of its orchid-rich meadows. The few that remain in the County must be managed in the traditional way, so that future generations may have some idea what the Suffolk countryside looked like before wide-spread ploughing, draining and spraying predominated in the County's agriculture.

The Suffolk Wildlife Trust, in co-operation with the County Highways, is protecting many species-rich stretches of roadside verges, a number of which contain orchids. The re-introduction of coppicing in a number of Suffolk woods is helping the woodland orchids to survive and increase. But the problem of raising the water level in the fens is, as yet, unsolved and it looks as if the Fen Orchid may have been lost from Suffolk. However, readers will be pleased to see that, as a result of Martin Sanford's well-organised survey of the present occurrence of orchids in Suffolk, one species, thought to have been lost from the County, has just been rediscovered flourishing in one of the few remaining unimproved Suffolk meadows.

Martin Sanford's painstaking research into herbaria and the literature is also most commendable. Alec Bull's comparison of the current habitats in the parish of Hitcham with Professor Henslow's account of the same parish early last century makes most interesting reading. The Suffolk Naturalists' Society is to be congratulated on publishing this book, which I hope will be the forerunner of many similar accounts of the orchids of other British counties.

June, 1990   Edgar Milne-Redhead,
                                                          Nayland, Suffolk

ACKNOWLEDGEMENTS

The Suffolk Orchid Survey (1985-1990) was organised by the Suffolk Biological Records Centre jointly funded by the Suffolk Naturalists' Society and Ipswich Borough Council. I am most grateful to the Society and the Borough Council for their commitment to the project.

Production of the distribution maps would have been impossible without the thousands of records provided by local societies and the many naturalists who took part in the survey; many thanks to all those who contributed information, particularly the principal recorders. I thank Dr. C. D. Preston of the Biological Records Centre, Monks Wood, for supplying details of many older records. The Suffolk Wildlife Trust and the Nature Conservancy Council have been most helpful in supplying records from their files. For access to various herbarium collections I thank Dr. A. G. Irwin (Castle Museum, Norwich) and the staff at the British Museum (Natural History) and the University of Cambridge Botany School. Mrs. G. Crompton and Mr. M. G. Rutterford have provided valuable information on Lizard Orchid. Thanks are also due to Dr. I. A. Denholm, Messrs. E. Milne-Redhead, A. L. Bull, F. W. Simpson, H. Mendel and Mrs. E. M. Hyde for their valuable advice and assistance. Dr. Alan Morton (Dept. of Pure and Applied Biology, Imperial College, Silwood Park, Ascot, Berks, SL5 7PY) has written the 'DMAP' software used to produce the distribution maps.

I thank all those who sent in photographs for consideration. The source of each of the original photographs is acknowledged in italics on the right-hand edge of each plate; special thanks to Dr. Rob Dryden for providing many excellent slides.

Finally, I thank my wife Katherine for her help with the text and for putting up with my obsession with orchids.

Principal Recorders

Rev. R. A. Addington	Mrs. E. M. Hyde
D. J. Addy	P. G. Lawson
M. Ausden	E. Milne-Redhead
D. Chittock	J. Muddeman
R. Cooke	E. W. Patrick
T. A. Craven	J. C. Roughton
J. W. Digby	J. Stone
Mrs. J. Harris	Mrs. S. Stone
Mrs. S. Hooton	R. Tofts
	J. Wakerley

Records were also received from :
Miss D. M. Abrahams, T. Abrehart, Dr. C. Beardall, Miss C. Beckett, J. Biglin, R. Blatch, W. Brame, A. L. Bull, Mrs. D. Casey, A. J. Cooper, Mrs. G. Crompton, J. T. Danter, Dr. I. A. Denholm, J. W. Drake, Dr. R. Dryden, R. D. Gadsby, Miss H. M. Gaught, Mrs. P. Gondris, Mrs. S. Gooch, M. Harding, D. Harpley, Mrs. Hobson, Mrs. M. Holdsworth, N. Hunt, M. A. Hyde, C. J. Jakes, I. J. Killeen, D. C. Lang, G. List, C. J. Lowe, A. Loweth, Mrs. F. Mankin, J. R. Martin, Mrs. T. Martin, H. Mendel, N. Miller, S. Mills, J. Minihane, A. Molyneux, Mrs. R. M. Narey, Mrs. S. O'Brien, A. Ost, Mrs. E. Parker, Mrs. M. Parker, E. Parsons, T. Peake, I. G. Pearson, Mrs. Perry, W. Peart, S. H. Piotrowski, R. Pitcher, Miss P. Pitty, R. E. Pole, Mrs. D. B. Radley, A. K. Rivett, A. A. Rowe, M. G. Rutterford, R. C. Shaw, Miss V. Sheldrake, C. Sheppard, P. Sheppy, Mrs. O. Sheppy, F. W. Simpson, C. Smith, D. F. Smith, J. Smithson, D. Strauss, J. Swann, R. S. Sweetman, B. Thompson, Lord Tollemache, P. J. O. Trist, Mrs. I. M. Vaughan, Miss L. Vulliamy, R. B. Warren, V. Watt, A. Williams, Miss B. Williamson, R. J. Woolnough, M. T. Wright.

INTRODUCTION

Orchids have a mysterious appeal which sets them apart from other groups of plants. Their exotic appearance and rarity engenders wide interest. In recent years the term 'orchid mania' has been used to describe the somewhat fanatical following the group has attracted. Some orchids have acquired the status of rare birds to be 'twitched', photographed or even dug up by unscrupulous collectors. This increased interest has added to our knowledge of the species but at the same time posed a threat. While there are those who for monetary or selfish reasons are willing to uproot and destroy plants, there is a necessary element of secrecy about the sites of very rare species. Some species, such as the Military Orchid near Mildenhall, now have high security fencing to prevent theft. It is often assumed that all orchids are rare, but there are still some half-a-dozen species in Suffolk that are quite widespread and under no immediate threat. Orchids are important 'indicator species'. Their habitat requirements are such that we can expect the places in which they are found to have particular qualities, like diversity and historical continuity, that make them valuable wildlife sites. They are often used as a measure in ecological evaluation and have become a symbol of the natural environment. The popular appeal of orchids makes them an ideal focus for raising support for habitat conservation.

ECOLOGY

The orchid family is one of the largest in the plant world, both in terms of the number of species and their geographical range. Much of its success is due to the way individual species are adapted to particular niches. Associations with mycorrhizal fungi have enabled many orchids to exploit habitats with poor nutrient or low light levels where competition from other plants is reduced. In the past the British countryside had many such habitats, the deep shade of the wildwood and the nitrogen-poor soils of fens and marshes, for example. Such areas, though often slow to establish, become stable for long periods. The 'plagioclimax' vegetation of chalk grassland and heathland, maintained by grazing, also provided habitats with nutrient-poor soils. A few species such as Twayblade and Common Spotted Orchid are 'generalists', able to colonise a variety of habitats. Others such as the Bog Orchid and the Bird's-nest Orchid have very precise habitat requirements. Many orchids are closely dependent on other species within their habitat – the mycorrhizal fungi, surrounding plants which provide shelter or substrate (e.g. Bog Orchid on *Sphagnum*), and specific insects for pollination. Complex and sometimes bizarre mechanisms to ensure pollination have evolved. Some species are unable to produce seed in the absence of specific insect pollinators.

For most orchids the presence of mycorrhizal fungi is essential even for the germination of seeds. The minute seeds are dependent on the fungus for nutrients and in many cases the association between fungus and plant continues even when the plant is mature. A few species like the Bird's-nest Orchid are devoid of chlorophyll and are entirely dependent on mycorrhizal fungi for the supply of nutrients from the breakdown of plant matter. Orchids are slow growing and can take at least four or five years from seed to flower. Most species are perennials and in ideal conditions will flower in succesive seasons over a period of years. It has been suggested that large clumps of the Purple Helleborine may be hundreds of years old. The Bee Orchid is normally a short-lived perennial, but in Britain, where optimum growth conditions for the Mediterranean species do not occur, it often exhausts itself producing the first flowering stem and dies having flowered only once (monocarpic).

VARIATION

One factor which makes orchids particularly interesting to study is their tendency to vary in colour, shape and scent. Variation in colour between individuals and populations is particularly common. This is often due to differences in the level of floral pigments called anthocyanins. These produce reds, purples and blues in flowers and, in combination with leaf pigments like chlorophyll, the purples and browns of leaf spots and stem and bract coloration. Variation in the amount of yellow pigments (anthoxanthins) is much rarer.

In some species, especially the dactylorchids, anthocyanin levels vary greatly to produce a whole range of flower colours between deep purple and white. Stem and leaf pigmentation is also very variable. Some of the more striking variations have been given varietal names such as the Leopard Marsh Orchid (*Dactylorhiza praetermissa* var. *pardalina*). The Early Marsh Orchid has a whole array of beautiful flower colours, produced by different levels of both anthocyanins and anthoxanthins, some of which have been given subspecific rank. In my experience dactylorchids with spotted leaves usually show a correlation between the amount of leaf spots and flower colour. In other species, such as the Early Purple Orchid, leaf and flower pigmentation are independent and plants of the same flower colour may have spotted or unspotted leaves. 'Albinos', with no floral pigments, are quite common in some species.

In species where flower colour is determined by both yellow and purple pigment types, partial 'albinos' may occur. These lack anthocyanins and are often green or yellow in colour. The Bee Orchid variety '*chlorantha*', and the yellow form of the Marsh Helleborine (*ochroleuca*) are examples. In other species anthocyanin levels may vary in response to the amount of sunlight. Man Orchids in open situations can turn a foxy red colour, while those in shade have yellow-green flowers. Similar changes can be seen in the Frog Orchid and the Broad-leaved Helleborine. The pigments act as a protection against high ultra violet light levels in the same way that melanin produces a sun tan in human skin. Species lacking either group of floral pigments, such as Butterfly Orchid and Autumn Lady's Tresses, show little or no variation in flower colour.

Some variations may be the result of different environmental conditions. The stunted plants of Southern Marsh Orchid found on dry chalk and the tall specimens of the Common Spotted Orchid that occur in deep shade are typical 'phenotypic' changes. Other variations, apparently caused by environmental conditions, may be due to genetic differences. The chalk grassland and marsh forms of Fragrant Orchid (ssp. *conopsea* and ssp. *densiflora*) are genetically distinct and have been given subspecific status. The Wasp Orchid (*Ophrys apifera* var. *trollii*) also comes into this category.

A further source of variation can be the result of mutation. In several species plants with radially symmetrical flowers have been found. In such flowers all petals may be shaped like the labellum or, more rarely, like the other petals. These abnormalities are termed 'peloria'; they have been seen in a few Suffolk orchids including the Green-winged Orchid (Sanford, 1986), the Early Marsh Orchid and the Early Purple Orchid. Other mutations may cause all flowers in a spike to be carried upside down. This has been found in Suffolk in Heath Spotted and Pyramidal Orchids. Variegated leaves have been found in several species and can spread vegetatively to form small colonies.

HABITATS

Grassland

Most species of orchids found in Suffolk are associated with grassland. Some, such as Early Purple and Common Spotted Orchids, appear to have been widespread in pastures in the 19th century, but are now mainly restricted to woodland. This does not show a change in habitat preference, but rather a severe loss of suitable pasture. Grazing pasture and hay meadows have been converted to arable throughout the past two centuries. Only a few of the once extensive commons and greens have escaped enclosure and encroachment. In the 17th and 18th centuries much of mid-Suffolk was a dairying district where long established management of grassland for grazing and hay had created flower-rich meadows. 19th century advances in agriculture led to the conversion of much of this pasture to arable use. In the 20th century grassland has suffered not only from the plough but from drainage, reseeding, fertilisers and herbicides. Many meadows have been reduced to monotonous grass and the remaining unimproved pastures are adversely affected by lack of grazing and the predominance of coarse grass. Several species are now restricted to woodland rides where the grass is cut on an annual basis and the soils are

Green-winged orchids at Chippenhall Green, old grassland protected by commoner's rights

undisturbed. The Common Spotted Orchid is perhaps the most typical of this group. Such species can still be found in grassland in the south of England where there are hay meadows or sheep grazing maintains suitable turf.

In Suffolk the few remaining commons and greens contain some of the best populations of species like the Green-winged Orchid. Suffolk Wildlife Trust reserves at Monewden, Mickfield, Framsden, Cransford and Metfield preserve tiny fragments of ancient meadow flora. Other grassland species survive around the edges of pits and quarries on short turf maintained by rabbits and on railway embankments not damaged by herbicides.

The more tolerant and adaptable species such as Bee and Pyramidal Orchids are still widespread on roadside verges. Verge management has changed greatly from the hand-mowing that survived in a few places into the 1950s. During the 60s and early 70s flail mowing 3-5 times a year inflicted serious damage, often preventing plants from flowering or setting seed. The cuttings were left to rot on the verges which encouraged the growth of rank vegetation at the expense of the herb-rich communities. In the late 70s a policy change resulted in little cutting at all. Increased fertility and the encroachment of scrub also damaged grassland communities. However, in a few areas good herb-rich swards have survived. Several of these sites are protected under a scheme run jointly by the Suffolk Wildlife Trust and the County Council Highways Department.

Most grassland orchids are dependent on the long-term stability of the habitat. Changes in drainage, addition of fertilisers, ploughing and reseeding or even changes in the cutting/grazing regime can often cause their decline. Research on Belgian nature reserves by Hermy & Vanecke (1989) has shown that with grassland Marsh Orchids population increase followed the introduction of management activities such as mowing. The creation of gaps in the 'standing crop' can result in exponential increase until optimal density is reached. Stopping or interrupting the mowing regime results in dereliction followed by a gradual decrease in numbers.

Chalk grassland was once widespread between Bury and Newmarket, where large areas were used for sheep grazing in the 18th and 19th centuries. The short-cropped turf was suitable for a number of species which are now extinct. Early Spider and Burnt Orchids are typical of the species found at one time on these pastures. Remnants of the flora of these vast areas survived at Saxham and further north at Risby Black Ditches, where Burnt Orchid survived until 1939. In the Breck chalk species were found on some of the ancient earthworks where excavation brought the pure chalk to the surface. Much of this area was enclosed by Parliamentary Acts between 1790 and 1840. Very large areas of open field and heathland were redesigned into large rectangular fields with straight roads and tracks. O.S. Maps of the 1830s clearly show the extent of the 'champion' or open field country. 'Risby Downs' and 'Fields' at Barrow, Gazeley, Moulton, Cavenham and Herringswell are still marked, although by that time much of this area was already enclosed. Newmarket Heath was also rich downland turf where Fragrant Orchid and Pasque Flower used to be found.

R. G. Dryden

Marsh Orchids at Melton Mead, a Suffolk Wildlife Trust reserve with a rich marsh flora

Fens and Marshes

Suffolk's wetlands have suffered great losses. Major projects from the end of the 18th century have completely changed the large fens in the north-west around Mildenhall and Lakenheath. Many smaller valley fens and headwater fens in the Breck have also been lost as a result of boreholes lowering the water table. Haslam (1965) gives an excellent account of the history and vegetation of fens in this area.

A few fens have survived in the Waveney/Little Ouse valley at Hopton, Market Weston, Thelnetham, and Redgrave. Apart from Market Weston, all have suffered in the 20th century from lowered water tables and invasion by scrub due to lack of management. Many of these fens were cut for peat, sedge and reeds, and water levels were carefully controlled. Acid bog habitat was present in several fens including delicate *Sphagnum* bogs with Sundews and Bog Orchids. Acid bogs could also be found in parishes north of Lowestoft in the early 19th century and, further south, a few survived until the 1930s in parishes like Butley and Chillesford. Barnby Broad has retained a similar flora to these fens, but most marshes in the Lowestoft area are grazed and consequently less diverse. Pakenham Fen, recently scheduled as a SSSI, contains several diverse wet meadows but has lost scarce species such as Frog and Fragrant Orchids.

Small marshes could be found throughout the County along minor river valleys. Many were drained quite early, using hollow 'bush drains'. The coastal grazing marshes are still quite extensive, but have mainly been 'improved' by reseeding and the application of fertilisers. Small areas retaining a rich flora can be found in parishes like Nacton, Theberton, Leiston and Benacre. Between the Orwell and Deben valleys there are still a number of wet pastures with large populations of Marsh Orchids.

Woodlands

Suffolk was less wooded than most counties even at the time of the Norman Conquest. Rackham (1980) calculates that in 1086 around 9% (84,000 acres) of the County was woodland or wood pasture. At that time the main concentration of woodland was in north-east Suffolk with very little in the Sandlings and none in the Breck. These woods were 'natural' though managed woods, not plantations, with a diversity of tree species. The next 200 years saw great changes in the landscape; by 1250 woodland was reduced to 6.5% (63,000 acres) of the County and there was a further 2% loss by 1350. Usually it was the larger woods that were destroyed first and by 1350 most of the big woods of the north-east had gone; most of the surviving woods were then in the south-west. Many of the woods that remained survived for the next 500 years. About 4.4% of the County (41,000 acres) was wooded in the 1830s when the first Ordnance Survey maps were produced. About half of that woodland has survived to the present day. During the Middle Ages new woods sometimes sprang up on land that went out of cultivation (e.g. a large part of Groton Wood). From the 17th century onwards landowners deliberately created plantations.

H. Mendel

Groton Wood, recently coppiced area with old Small-leaved Lime coppice behind

Typical ancient woods in Suffolk include those at Bradfield and Barking, Bull's Wood Cockfield, Combs Wood, Middle Wood Offton and part of Groton Wood. Many of these woods are characterised by a particular assemblage of plants which can be used as 'indicator species'. Several orchids come into this category, including Purple Helleborine, Greater Butterfly, Bird's-nest and to some extent, Early Purple Orchid. These species show little or no ability to colonise new sites. Rackham (1980) details the changes in management that have occurred in our ancient woods. For orchids, one of the most significant changes was the decline in coppicing in the late 19th and early 20th centuries. Woods had been managed as 'coppice with standards' with a gradually lengthening rotation from around six years in the 13th century to fourteen or fifteen years in the 19th century. Ash, Maple, Hazel, Sallow, Elm, and Small-leaved Lime were all coppiced, usually with Oak or Ash as the standards. These rotations, continued over hundreds of years, had created a subtle range of successional habitats. Much of this was lost as, without management, rides became choked and heavy shade over long periods in the overgrown coppice stands broke the succession, to the detriment of many species. By 1950 traditional coppice management had virtually ceased in the County, apart from the famous woods at Bradfield. Littlewood (1982) gives details of many ancient woods on mid-Suffolk boulder clay.

SOIL REGIONS

Soil factors limit the ranges of most orchids and many of the distribution maps reflect the dependence of species on particular soil types. The majority of species are associated to some extent with base-rich, alkaline soils. Heath Spotted Orchid is the only species remaining in the County which prefers acid soils. Modern agriculture has had a neutralising effect on many soils. Drainage and the addition of lime in acid areas and the application of nitrate fertilisers in alkaline areas has greatly reduced the diversity of grasslands.

Suffolk's soils are mostly derived from glacial 'drift', which masks the solid geology (chalk in west and central Suffolk, crag in the east). Two thirds of the County is covered by a mantle of chalky boulder clay. It is flanked to the east and west by large areas of sandy soils. In the west these cover chalk, while in the extreme north-west the sands dip beneath the peats of the fen basin. In the east great expanses of sand overlie the crag deposits except in the Shotley and Felixstowe peninsulas, where the covering is a wind-blown loess known as cover-loam.

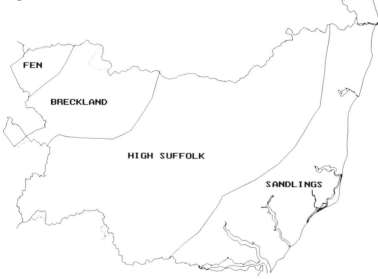

In the 18th century, the mid-Suffolk clay was known as the 'Wood-lands', the sands of the north-west the 'Fielding' and the coastal sands as the 'Sandlands'. At that time there were still areas of blowing sand in the east and in the north-west large areas of sand were mobile in several parishes. In the 19th century these names changed. The Fielding was split into the wet 'Fen' of the north-west and the dry heaths of the 'Breck' district (the name 'Breckland' was first coined by W. G. Clarke in 1894). The central clay lands were known as 'High Suffolk' and the heaths and sheep walks of the coastal strip were called 'Sandlings'.

SUFFOLK ORCHIDS,
HALF A CENTURY OF CHANGE

Francis Simpson

Our wild orchids fascinate so many botanists and naturalists that many species have suffered at the hands of over enthusiastic collectors and even photographers may damage their habitats by trampling. In recent years further interest has been aroused by the publication of a number of floras detailing habitats and sites where they can be found. I hope this book will not encourage still more people to collect specimens or to dig them up for their gardens or for sale, a practice which all too frequently endangers rare species.

F W Simpson

Common Spotted and Butterfly Orchids at Lineage Wood, 1939

Seventy years ago when I began exploring the Suffolk countryside on foot and by bicycle I found my first orchids, the Early Purple on a roadside verge between Tuddenham and Swilland and in woods at Bramford. One of my most delightful early experiences was on one early June morning, when shortly after entering a wood about ten miles from Ipswich, I found a number of the most lovely Greater Butterfly Orchid and Common Spotted Orchid. The scene was so beautiful, a perfect sunny day, the fresh growth of the trees and bushes and other flora, and the wonderful chorus of bird song with never a silent moment. It is not like that today. The woods I used to know so well have changed, they have not the numbers of orchids or their singing birds. I told a master at the school I was attending about my find of the Butterfly Orchids as he was interested in wild flowers and had given me a small flora. He visited this wood and told me that he saw children there picking the orchids like weeds. I explored this wood many times and found there also Early Purple, Twayblade and a few Broad-leaved Helleborine and Fly Orchid.

The Greater or Wood Butterfly Orchid I found in various numbers in nearly all the old chalky boulder clay woods and copses and sometimes outside woods on rough pastures. I remember once walking through a wood near Stowmarket at dusk and the air was filled with the scent of this orchid which attracts moths with long tongues to sample the drop of nectar at the tip of the spur.

The Early Purple and Common Spotted Orchids have always been very frequent and sometimes abundant in woods and old pastures. However, I have seen the destruction of many of their former habitats. We have lost several important orchid and flora-rich woods where I used to spend many happy days. Other woods have been much reduced in size or changed beyond recognition by management and planting of alien trees or the intensive farming and drainage of surrounding areas. Lucy Wood, Elmsett, was destroyed. This was one of the ancient Oxlip woods with its rich associated flora of Orchids; Early Purple, Butterfly, Common Spotted, Twayblade and Broad-leaved Helleborine. Herb Paris and other species were a delight to see every year. Elmsett Park, also an ancient wood which once extended to about three hundred acres, had many orchids and other interesting flora, much of which still exists in the area not damaged by industrial use.

Another wonderful habitat destroyed was Middle Grove with Horse Pasture Grove and the surrounding rough pastures at Finborough. Middle Grove had been one of the best Oxlip sites in Suffolk, carpeting much of the Grove in the greatest profusion. On the edge and outside, the Butterfly Orchid grew in large numbers, in some years more than one hundred flowering spikes. There were also Common Spotted and a few Fly Orchids and Helleborines.

I used to find the Violet Helleborine in several woods in West Suffolk, i.e. at Bull's Cross, Milden, Little Cornard and Assington. Another orchid I used to find regularly in the ancient woods which had not been coppiced for many years was the Bird's-nest. I saw it first at Great Bealings in the late twenties in a wood recorded in the Domesday Survey. I saw it most years in several woods which were once part of the extensive Milden Thicks and also in Barking Woods.

The Twayblade is one of my favourite orchids. I found it very frequently in many woods and old damp pastures in nearly every parish. I saw it at Newbourn in the early twenties where it still occurs much as it did in those early days.

The most frequent and abundant of all our orchids in Suffolk is the Southern Marsh, which I used to call the Common Marsh. It was extremely plentiful in many river valleys in wet meadows and marshes. Many specimens in favourable habitats have huge flowering spikes. However, some of the largest specimens with spotted leaves were obviously hybrids with Spotted Orchids, either the Common Spotted or the Heath Spotted. I saw the species and hybrids at their finest in the valley of the Butley River to Chillesford, the Mill River between Foxhall and Newbourn, at Sizewell Belts and between Thorpeness and Aldeburgh, at Polstead and Bromeswell where one good habitat was destroyed by tipping. The Heath Spotted has always been less frequent than the Common Spotted and restricted mainly to marshes on sandy acid soils where there is bracken. I found it in plenty in two small valleys at Martlesham and really abundant at Kirton, where it just survives in a much reduced area.

Before the last war the Green-winged Meadow Orchid was frequent in very many then untreated meadows, pastures and parks. One had only to look and there it was. I remember these lovely orchids in Hintlesham and Brettenham Parks, in meadows at Bentley, Polstead, Barking, Naughton and Hasketon. In two small narrow meadows at Waldringfield, where both the Early Purple and the Green-winged grew, I found what was obviously the rare hybrid between the species. These meadows no longer exist.

There was hardly a Suffolk parish where orchids could not be found. Even within the Borough of Ipswich there were Southern Marsh, Common Spotted and their hybrids in areas of the Dales Road Brickfield. A nice colony of the Heath Spotted survived in the little valley with its Red Crag spring and stream from Beggar's Hollow off Clapgate Lane. This valley was filled up with rubbish to make the Landseer Road Recreation ground. Bee Orchids were seen on the Railway embankment between Dale Hall Lane and Westerfield. There were also Heath Spotted in the Bucklesham Road swamps.

The Frog Orchid was always difficult to find, but it was in many of the old horse pastures if you searched. Specimens were usually quite small or trodden down. I saw it regularly at Barking, Felsham and Naughton.

The Man or Green Man Orchid was more frequent in the areas where it is still recorded. In the Blood Hill Chalk Pit, Bramford, I found it in fair numbers. This old pit was a wonderful habitat for its flora and butterflies. Now it has been used as a rubbish tip. Round the top edge of that pit and in the Little Blakenham Chalk Pit there used to be many fine specimens and I saw it also on four roadside verges and banks. It was always at Nedging in and around a small chalk pit where there were Fly Orchids. Another nice colony was found on the grassy verge of the drive, then rarely mown, leading to Nedging Church. There were also several on the roadside verge between Semer and Nedging and I found a colony on an old lane bank at Nedging Tye.

The Bee Orchid was frequent, sometimes abundant, in some years, especially on the chalky boulder clay in rough uncultivated fields, on the grassy slopes of quarries and even on roadside banks and verges. There was a good habitat at Stowmarket on the site of a former Gun Cotton Factory. Here also were Pyramidal Orchids, a species which favoured the same habitats.

The Fly Orchid I found at eleven sites. There was a good colony which used to grow near a large number of Butterfly and Common Spotted Orchids at Lineage Wood, Long Melford.

Before the last war, I used to cycle in June and July from Ipswich to Redgrave and Thelnetham Fens to see the various orchids. The Fragrant was often flowering in considerable abundance. There were also some fine colonies of the Marsh Helleborine. The Early Marsh Orchid was frequent in these Fens. Elsewhere in Suffolk that species was never common. The Fen Orchid I used to see at three sites. At one there were at least a hundred specimens. It was then such a good habitat with the three species of Sundew, Butterwort and Grass of Parnassus.

It was on Thursday afternoon 27th June, 1935, that I found a single specimen of the Lizard Orchid on the edge of a Coralline Crag pit in Sudbourne Park. Some years later I discovered a small colony on the site of the former Gun Cotton Factory at Stowmarket. This area has now been reclaimed.

The Autumn Lady's Tresses I only saw on the lawn of the old Rectory at Whatfield in the 1930s. Ronald Burn, a botanist, lived there when his father was the Rector.

Several Suffolk orchids I never found; the Bog, Musk, Early Spider, Burnt and Creeping Lady's Tresses. I used to search all the old sites recorded in Hind's Flora of 1889. The Military Orchid was unknown in the County. The chalk pit at Mildenhall where it now grows was, in the early thirties before the planting of the Conifers, part of an extensive rabbit warren. We certainly gained a lovely species.

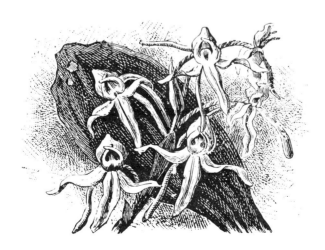

CONSERVATION

One third of the species of orchid recorded from Suffolk has become extinct. Four species have been lost this century, one in the last thirty years. Another ten species are barely surviving with very few sites. All of the species except Military Orchid (which only ever had one site), have shown some reduction in range and numbers of sites (see Table 2.). These losses are paralleled in other groups such as butterflies (Mendel & Piotrowski, 1986).

The importance of orchids as indicators of ancient and often diverse habitats allows us to infer that many other species of plants and insects will also have declined. Individual orchid species can be found in a wide range of habitats covering most of the major 'semi-natural' ecosystems. Conservation aimed at orchids will therefore benefit a very wide range of species of both plants and insects.

A few species have never been frequent in the County. For some, their precise habitat requirements are naturally in short supply. Others, like the Lizard Orchid, are on the edge of their climatic range; changes in numbers are often due to quite minor changes in climate over a number of years. Several species reach their northern and western limits in Britain. Species like the Creeping Lady's Tresses and perhaps even the Military Orchid may occur as the result of chance introductions of seed or plants. For all these species conservation is particularly difficult and we can often do little more than protect individual localities as reserves. Species on the edges of their range are often more sensitive than normal. They may be the first to react to minor changes in habitat or climate. Constant monitoring of such sensitive populations is very important, particularly for sites away from the main distribution, where there is little chance of re-colonisation.

Rare species are also in danger from collectors and flower pickers. Simpson (1982) suggests that collectors may have been an important factor in the loss of the Fen Orchid in the 1970s. Drainage had already resulted in it becoming very scarce and such rarities are a great attraction to those of a 'stamp collecting' mentality. Even the protection of some species under the Wildlife and Countryside Act (1981) with a maximum penalty of £2000 for digging up or picking plants has not deterred some fanatics.

Although factors like climate have affected a few species most extinctions have resulted from of Man's activities. For all the remaining species, habitat destruction remains the most important threat to their continued existence. Agricultural changes have created and destroyed a whole succession of habitats. As far as orchids are concerned, habitats have become less and less stable with subtle changes in management practices often having as much effect as more drastic measures like drainage.

Hitcham

The parish of Hitcham provides a valuable case history of the decline in orchid numbers that has occurred over the past 140 years. It is of average size (4300 acres) and is situated near the middle of the County on chalky boulder clay.

At one time it was rich in suitable orchid habitats with ancient woodland, undisturbed grassland and many wet areas of springs and streams. We are fortunate in that it has been home to two excellent botanists – the Rev. J. S. Henslow and Mr. A. L. Bull, who have provided us with detailed records for the periods 1840-1860 and 1945-1961. Henslow first moved to Hitcham in 1837 and stayed until his death in 1861; he left a list of plants found in the parish over nearly 25 years. As well as his work with Skepper on the 1860 Flora, he produced an excellent herbarium (now at Ipswich Museum) with much of the material provided by pupils of the parish school. He also contributed specimens to herbaria at Cambridge, London and Norwich. In all Henslow found thirteen orchid species in the parish. Another two species have been recorded more recently but must have been present at that time and were not known to Henslow. Records are summarised in Table 1.

Table 1. Orchids at Hitcham

	Henslow's records (1840-1860)	Bull's records (1945-1961)
Man	1840-1858	–
Pyramidal	-1860	1945
Frog	1849	1945-1950
Common Spotted	1842	1945-1959
Heath Spotted	–	1951-1961
Southern Marsh	1850	1945-1959
Fragrant	1850	1945-1950
Twayblade	-1860	1945-1959
Bird's-nest	-1860	–
Bee	1847	1945
Fly	-1860	1959
Early Purple	1842	1954
Green-winged	1850	1954-1960
Butterfly	1857	1945-1959

Alec Bull did much botanising at Hitcham in the 1940s and 50s (Bull, 1945 & 1977) and added Heath Spotted Orchid to the list of species found by Henslow. This species was not recognised as separate from the Common Spotted until 1915. Although it must have been present at the time it would not have been recorded by Henslow. Simpson (1982) records Broad-leaved Helleborine from Hitcham; this species may well have been present in Henslow's day but have been overlooked.

Of the fourteen species present in the parish in Henslow's day all but two, Man and Bird's-nest Orchid, were refound by Bull. Man Orchid must have been quite frequent in the 19th century; there are at least five specimens in various herbaria all collected at Hitcham between 1840 and 1860. It is odd that it was not refound by Bull as it was still present a few miles away in the nearby parishes of Wattisham, Nedging and Semer in the 1950s. The survival

Man Orchid from Hitcham, collected by Rev. J. S. Henslow, 1849

of species like Fly, Frog and Fragrant Orchid in this parish is most surprising. Frog and Fragrant Orchid had been lost from most of the County before 1900 and the Fly was only recorded in six sites post-1950.

Only four species have been recorded from Hitcham post-1980. Ancient woodland with Twayblade and Common Spotted Orchids still exists at Home Wood, though much of it has been coniferised. Early Purple Orchid can be found at Consent Wood. The parish has been covered well by Mrs. J. Harris and several other competent botanists. Pyramidal Orchid was re-found on a roadside verge in the parish in 1990, but it is unlikely that many other species are still present.

Ironically, some loss of habitats in Suffolk may have been indirectly due to the efforts of the Rev. Henslow as an agricultural reformer. He discovered the potential of coprolite nodules as an artificial manure and made great efforts to educate the farming community on the benefits of scientific agricultural practice. It appears the local farmers of Hitcham were not happy to be dictated to by their local parson (Russell-Gebbett, 1977) and his discourses probably had more effect in areas further afield.

Bull (1977) gives a fascinating account of the changes that have occurred in this parish. Rich ancient woodland floras were lost with the clearance of Hitcham Wood (102 acres) and Eastwood (100 acres) around 1860 (the Ely Coucher Book of 1251 refers to 250 acres of woodland at Hitcham); this accounts for the disappearance of Bird's-nest Orchid. Many smaller woodland fragments were grubbed out between the wars. Large areas of grazing and hay pasture, including many wet and marshy areas, were drained and ploughed up. Much ploughing occurred during the two World Wars with the increased demand for home food production. The few old pastures that survived into the 1950s (including the only site for the grassland form of Fragrant Orchid, *Gymnadenia conopsea* ssp. *conopsea*, in the County) suffered a similar fate and were either cleared and reseeded or had artificial fertilisers applied. This use of fertilisers to increase yield has had a devastating effect on the few remaining ancient meadows. The diversity of species in these undisturbed sites is dependent on low nutrient levels preventing too much competition from rank grasses. Chalk grassland species such as Man, Bee and Pyramidal Orchids soon became restricted to roadside verges and old driftways where small areas of undisturbed habitat remained. During the 1960s and 70s herbicides drifting from arable crop spraying must have destroyed most of these refuges.

Comparison of modern records with those from the 19th century shows that the decline at Hitcham is far from unique. Daniel Stock, (a major contributor to the 'New Botanist's Guide', see Morley, 1946) recorded a dozen species from the Bungay area in the 1830s. His records include the Narrow-leaved Helleborine (*Cephalanthera longifolia*) at the foot of the Bath Hills on the Norfolk side of the Waveney. Much of this area has now become an 'arable desert'; the only orchids likely to be found are Pyramidal and Bee on sheltered roadside verges. Other rich parishes such as Great Glemham,

Pakenham, Great Barton and Theberton have all witnessed a severe decline in the number of species. The greatest periods of loss appear to have been conversion of semi-natural habitats to arable during the 'agricultural revolution' of the early 19th century and in the first and second World Wars and an even more damaging intensive farming revolution during the last forty years.

Since 1945 fundamental changes in the structure and methods of farming have brought about changes as significant as those which occurred during the enclosure movement. Fields have become larger, hedgerows have disappeared and the farming economy has become almost entirely arable. Even by 1955 79% of agricultural land in the County was arable. The rate of change accelerated after 1960. Efficiency encouraged the creation of larger fields which are ploughed right to the edge. Grant aid was available for draining, reseeding and fertilising the few remaining areas of permanent grass. New and more effective herbicides and fungicides were developed and with increased investment in the land these expensive techniques became widespread.

After the war the human population started to increase again. During the 1960s it rose by 15% and the boom has continued in the 1970s and 80s. Some of this increase has been taken up by the towns, but there have also been expansions of many rural villages, often in conjunction with the development of new industrial estates. These changes have inevitably resulted in the destruction of orchid habitats. Other major developments like the Nuclear Power Stations at Sizewell have also taken up important areas of semi-natural habitat. New roads have been built to cope with the huge increases in traffic over the past 30 years. In some places road building has provided important new verge habitats which, with suitable management, may provide new sites for orchids.

The idea of conservation of habitats through creation of nature reserves is quite a recent phenomenon. Suffolk's first reserve, at Mickfield, was created only fifty years ago and it is interesting to note that as late as 1946 it was proposed that Redgrave Fen should be used as a practice bombing site for the Air Ministry!

Protection of sites through the creation of reserves and, in Suffolk, protected roadside verges, has been essential for the survival of several species. For Marsh and Purple Helleborines, Lizard, Military, Frog, Fly, and Narrow-leaved Marsh Orchids all of the known sites in the County are scheduled by the Nature Conservancy Council as Sites of Special Scientific Interest (SSSIs). Many of these sites are also managed as reserves by the Suffolk Wildlife Trust. Edgar Milne-Redhead, assisted by Peter Lawson of the Suffolk Wildlife Trust, has promoted the very successful protected roadside verge scheme in association with Suffolk County Council Highways Department. This has been very effective in the protection and management of sites for several grassland species. Verges contain nearly all the known sites for Man Orchid and are very important for the Pyramidal Orchid.

SSSIs as specified in the Wildlife and Countryside Act (1981) do not give the protection that was intended by Parliament, and many have been damaged and some lost in consequence. The Wildlife and Countryside Act needs amending to prevent loss of sites. The sad loss of one of the best sites for Green-winged Orchids in Essex through wilful destruction by the land-owner in 1985 pointed out the loopholes in the present legislation.

On nature reserves careful study of the precise requirements of species is needed to ensure that management is suitable. Long-term monitoring of populations can provide vital information on the effectiveness of management regimes. Care should be taken to avoid confusing the effects of changing weather from year to year on numbers of flowering plants with the effects of specific management on orchid populations.

There have been a few instances in which conservationists have resorted to transplanting turf containing orchids from threatened sites. People have even tried moving plants to their own gardens for 'protection'. Given the complex life-cycle, precise soil requirements and mycorrhizal associations of orchids this has to be a very hit-and-miss affair. One of the main dangers of this process is that, whether successful or not, it sets a precedent which developers of other sites may try and follow. It should only be used as an extreme last resort when there is no possibility of leaving the plants *in situ*.

Research has shown that orchid seeds remain viable for only a few months and there is no build-up of a seed bank in the soil. Recent work on micropropagation of native orchids has suggested it is possible to propagate plants in sufficient numbers to reintroduce them to the wild. The Sainsbury project, set up at the Royal Botanic Gardens at Kew in 1983, has been successful in propagating a number of native species. The rate of success with reintroductions of orchids, having been sown *in vitro*, has increased from 15% in 1984 to 30% in 1989, mainly due to a better knowledge of the growing conditions of existing orchid habitats. It is still a difficult procedure and care must be taken when choosing sites, so that the natural distribution of these species is not affected. Ronse (1989) provides a good overview of the subject of *in vitro* propagation and reintroductions.

Secrecy about sites for very rare species is a sad necessity while there are still collectors wishing to dig plants up. It also helps to protect sensitive sites from trampling hordes of photographers and 'orchid twitchers'. However, such secrecy can also endanger sites if it means objections are not made when sites come up for development or a landowner changes the management. Not all sites for orchids are protected as SSSIs or nature reserves and unless details of their whereabouts are housed at a local records centre or similar place of safe-keeping there is always the chance that sites will be destroyed because their value was not made known. We must ensure that even the smallest orchid site is not lost through neglect.

After decades of ever increasing agricultural expansion it now seems as if the tide may be turning. Grants and subsidies for grain production are being reduced and for the first time there may be financial incentives to leave land fallow or even create new habitats. This sort of activity needs very careful planning. It is not as simple as letting fields 'fall down to grass'; without management such areas will rapidly fill with scrub and in the long term become secondary woodland. Rackham (1986) has pointed out the dangers of indiscriminate habitat creation without reference to existing landscapes and traditional practices. The present EEC 'set aside' scheme is a short term measure which does not ensure that land will not be brought back into cultivation in the future. This may benefit those species, such as Bee and Pyramidal Orchids, which are capable of quickly colonising new habitats, but it does not create the stable management over long periods of time required by the majority of species. So far there is little to suggest that the rate of habitat destruction as a result of modern farming and urban development is slowing down. No new permanent grasslands are being created in which orchids might flourish and the few remaining fragments of semi-natural habitats are constantly being damaged.

THE SUFFOLK ORCHID SURVEY

The Suffolk Orchid Survey was launched in 1985 to assess the distribution and status of each of the species found in the County. Initially, a key to the identification of Suffolk orchids and recording cards were distributed to a large number of recorders. After the first year all the records and a large amount of historical data were collated to produce a provisional atlas. This greatly aided recording by stimulating recorders to fill in the gaps and to update older records. In addition to the efforts of the principal recorders there were many records provided by members of the public in response to publicity about the survey. All records were fed into the computer at the Suffolk Biological Records Centre to enable quick retrieval and sorting. Maps were produced using the computer so that updates could quickly be printed out for the following year's fieldwork. Accuracy of recording was high, with most confusion being caused by the variable marsh and spotted orchids. Pro-forma recording sheets were used to ensure that records were provided with accurate grid references and dates. The majority of records from the survey period have six-figure grid references.

Three years' field survey has still not produced total coverage, but all of the major habitats have been covered and in most cases the maps do show accurate distributions. Unlike the Butterfly Survey (Mendel & Piotrowski, 1986), there are many squares where no species can be found. This does not mean that the area has not been searched. Numbers of flower spikes can fluctuate greatly from year to year. Some species, such as the Autumn Ladies Tresses, which may produce hundreds or even thousands of flower spikes in an uncut lawn or pasture, apparently disappear for many years when mown. A survey period of three years may well miss sites for these more erratic species. Gaps in coverage show up most with the commoner species. There are still many small pockets of ancient woodland which have not yet been searched, where Early Purples or Twayblades might be found. It is also likely that a few wet meadows with small numbers of Southern Marsh Orchids have been overlooked. For these species the major aim of the survey was to establish distribution patterns and frequency and this is quite apparent from the maps. The coverage map (Coverage Map 1.) does pick out those areas which have high numbers of orchids; these are nearly all ancient woodland sites or squares with both marsh and woodland habitats. When older records (Coverage Map 2.) are compared with those made from 1980 onwards (Coverage Map 3.) the loss of species from the mid-Suffolk ancient woodlands is clearly shown.

Research in literature and correspondence housed at the Suffolk Biological Records Centre and Ipswich Museum and in a number of local and national herbaria produced a very large number of historical records. These have provided much of the background for comparison with modern distributions. In some cases older records can show a species' continuity at a particular site over one hundred years or more. The records for the parish of Hitcham given in an earlier section are a good example of how useful such records can be in monitoring change.

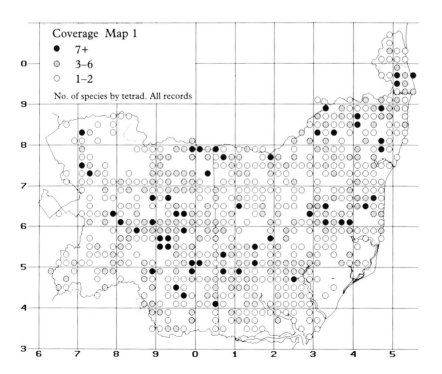

Coverage Map 1
● 7+
◉ 3–6
○ 1–2

No. of species by tetrad. All records

28

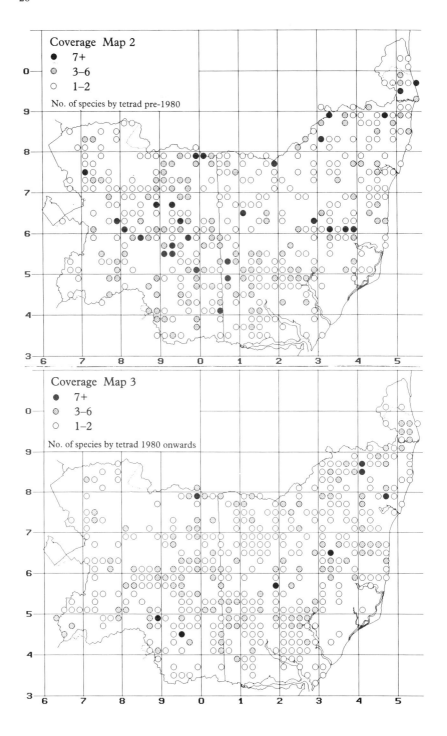

THE CATALOGUE

A total of thirty-two species of orchid have been recorded from Suffolk. Ten species have already become extinct and another ten are now very rare in the County. Eight different hybrids have been found, mainly in the *Dactylorhiza* group. With the exception of Creeping Lady's Tresses (*Goodyera repens*), all the species can be regarded as native to Suffolk.

Table 2. Checklist and status of Species

Doubtful Species

White Helleborine	*Cephalanthera damasonium*
Narrow-leaved Helleborine	*Cephalanthera longifolia*

Extinctions -1900

		Last record
Bog Orchid	*Hammarbya paludosa*	c.1840
Musk Orchid	*Herminium monorchis*	c.1820
Lesser Butterfly Orchid	*Platanthera bifolia*	c.1880
Early Spider Orchid	*Ophrys sphegodes*	1793

Extinctions 1900-1990

Green-flowered Helleborine	*Epipactis phyllanthes*	pre-1970
Creeping Lady's Tresses	*Goodyera repens*	1935
Fen Orchid	*Liparis lœselii*	1974
Burnt Orchid	*Orchis ustulata*	1939

One site 1980 onwards

Frog Orchid	*Cœloglossum viride*
Military Orchid	*Orchis militaris*
Autumn Lady's Tresses	*Spiranthes spiralis*

Five or less sites 1980 onwards

Man Orchid	*Aceras anthropophorum*
Narrow-leaved Marsh Orchid	*Dactylorhiza traunsteineri*
Marsh Helleborine	*Epipactis palustris*
Violet Helleborine	*E. purpurata*
Fragrant Orchid	*Gymnadenia conopsea*
Lizard Orchid	*Himantoglossum hircinum*
Fly Orchid	*Ophrys insectifera*

Scarce 1980 onwards

Early Marsh Orchid	*Dactylorhiza incarnata*
Heath Spotted Orchid	*D. maculata* ssp. *ericetorum*
Broad-leaved Helleborine	*Epipactis helleborine*
Bird's-nest Orchid	*Neottia nidus-avis*
Green-winged Orchid	*Orchis morio*
Greater Butterfly Orchid	*Platanthera chlorantha*

Frequent 1980 onwards

Pyramidal Orchid	*Anacamptis pyramidalis*
Common Spotted Orchid	*Dactylorhiza fuchsii*
Southern Marsh Orchid	*D. prætermissa*
Twayblade	*Listera ovata*
Bee Orchid	*Ophrys apifera*
Early Purple Orchid	*Orchis mascula*

Checklist of hybrids

Dactylorhiza fuchsii × incarnata

D. fuchsii × maculata ssp. *ericetorum*

D. fuchsii × prætermissa

D. incarnata × prætermissa

D. maculata ssp. *ericetorum × prætermissa*

D. prætermissa × traunsteineri

Epipactis helleborine × purpurata

Orchis mascula × morio

The Text

For each species a brief description of the more important features for identification is given; these are intended only to help distinguish similar species. Detailed information for each species can be found in Summerhayes (1968) and Lang (1980). Flowering periods and habitat notes refer to Suffolk where the data is available. My comments and inferences appear in square brackets, quotations are in italics. Nomenclature follows Simpson (1982) and Stace (1975).

The Maps

The survey area covers the Watsonian vice-counties of East and West Suffolk. Where the administrative boundaries differ from the vice-counties they have been indicated by a dotted line. Details of vice-county boundaries are given in Mendel (1984). Records are plotted by tetrads, blocks of four 1 km squares (the smallest units on the 1:50,000 Ordnance Survey maps). Only records from within Suffolk (vice-counties 25 and 26) have been plotted for tetrads straddling the border. Maps have been produced on a laser printer using 'DMAP' software written by Dr. Alan Morton.

For all maps except the Fly Orchid the following date classes have been used:-

    ○ 1800-1959   ◉ 1960-1979   ● 1980-1990

Undated records have been included in the earliest date class. All records, whether recent or historical, have been plotted. Where records from two date classes coincide, only the most recent has been plotted. This technique clearly shows contractions of range, but effectively obscures any expansions. For orchids this is not a problem, as none of the species in Suffolk has been in a position to expand its range.

MAN ORCHID *Aceras anthropophorum* (L.) Ait. f.

The characteristic yellowish-green, man-shaped flowers of this species make it easy to identify. It is quite a stout plant with tall flower spikes, but these are very difficult to spot when growing in tall grass. The basal leaves are broad and bluish-green, the upper leaves are narrow and clasp the stem. The flowers are out from early May to June and are often tinged reddish-brown, especially in sunny situations. Their cryptic coloration blends in well with the surrounding vegetation and they rely on a rather unpleasant smell to attract insects. The species has a strong preference for dry chalky soils and is usually found in open situations or amongst light scrub. It is often found around the edges of chalk quarries and pits. In Britain the Man Orchid has a southern distribution, being commonest in the south-east with a similar range to the Lizard Orchid. Both these species appear to have undergone population fluctuations which may be linked to climatic changes.

The Man Orchid is now very rare in Suffolk, with three of the remaining four sites being on protected roadside verges. As this orchid comes into growth in November and December and goes on growing during the early spring months, it is not killed by the grass being cut in May, but is prevented from flowering and seeding. It may well still occur undetected on some other roadside verges in Suffolk. It was first discovered at Flowton in 1986 when the verge was newly protected from a May cut to enable the Sulphur Clover

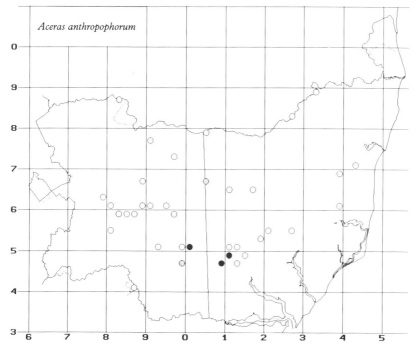

Man Orchid

(*Trifolium ochroleucon*) to be seen in flower, and the Man Orchid was also able to flower! At Wattisham it has survived close mowing on a private verge for many years and at Nedging it survived under similar conditions, with the Adder's Tongue Fern, (*Ophioglossum vulgatum*). At Little Blakenham it occurs on a verge and on the edge of a nearby chalk pit. It has grown around these pits for many years. According to R. S. Sweetman (pers. comm. 1988) the plants at Wattisham had more purple-tinged flowers than those at the other sites. Unlike some other chalk- loving species it has not been found on crag soils and is mainly restricted to pure chalk in the Gipping valley and a small area of particularly chalky boulder clay around Hitcham, Wattisham and Nedging.

It was probably never frequent in the County, Hind (1889) lists 27 sites several of which are from Henslow & Skepper's earlier Flora. It was well known in a number of West Suffolk parishes before 1850. Sir John Cullum found it by a chalk pit at Ickworth Park in 1778 (Boreham, 1962). Several herbarium specimens were collected at Stanton in the 1830s and it was recorded and collected at Hitcham by Henslow for many years. The relatively large number of herbarium specimens from this period does not necessarily indicate that the species was common. Victorian collectors were more interested in the rare and unusual species and in the case of Man Orchid specimens all originate from a very small number of sites. Much of the decrease occurred during the late 19th century when many chalky pastures were ploughed up. Some suitable habitats were destroyed during the two World Wars both for agricultural use and in a few cases for the creation of airfields. In the east of the County it survived on verges at Bacton, Swilland and Otley until about 1960, but was probably lost due to inappropriate cutting regimes or drifting herbicide spray. The best populations have occurred around the chalk pits at Blakenham and Bramford. Simpson (1937) noted more than fifty spikes on the edge of the quarry at Blood Hill, Bramford prior to its re-opening in 1935. The superb chalk flora of the pits at Bramford and Blakenham has been disturbed several times as pits have been reopened for extraction of chalk for liming fields and more recently for use as land-fill sites. Plants have been moved from an endangered site in Bramford to a nearby Suffolk Wildlife Trust reserve. At this site a small remnant of the typical chalk flora can be seen with Wild Thyme (*Thymus pulegioides*), Rockrose (*Helianthemum nummularium*) and Stemless Thistle (*Cirsium acaule*).

PYRAMIDAL ORCHID
Anacamptis pyramidalis (L.) L. C. M. Rich.

This charming species gets its name from the shape of the flower spikes. These are conical as the first flowers come out, but later become more domed or spherical as more flowers open. The narrow pointed leaves form an over-wintering rosette which has usually withered by the time the slender flower stems appear in mid-June and July. The tightly packed flowers are usually a bright rose pink with no markings; variations from deep red through to white

R. G. Dryden

Pyramidal Orchid

can be found. Individual flowers are quite elegant in shape with small upper petals and sepals and a dainty three-lobed lip. The labellum has two upright plates at the base which are angled towards the base of the long spur. The lobes are equal in size and spreading. It is a widespread species on dry calcareous soils throughout England, Ireland and the west of Scotland. It is found more often amongst taller grasses and herbs than are many grassland orchids.

In Suffolk it is still well distributed throughout the central strip of boulder clay. It has very similar requirements to the Bee Orchid and the two species can often be found at the same site. Some of the best populations are to be found on exposed chalk in the Gipping valley around Blakenham and Coddenham. It is also quite frequent in the north-east around 'the Saints' of the South Elmhams and Ilketshalls where it is often associated with another species typical of the boulder clay, Sulphur Clover (*Trifolium ochroleucon*). The majority of its sites in the County are on roadside verges. At Great Blakenham it grows in great profusion on a protected roadside verge near the Blue Circle cement factory. Associated species include Bee Orchid (including a few var. *chlorantha*), Ploughman's Spikenard (*Inula conyza*) and Wild Parsnip (*Pastinaca sativa*). It grows on other protected verges at Rickinghall, Earl Stonham, Rishangles, Framlingham, Kelsale, Long Melford, Hawkedon, Brockley, Whepstead, and Felsham. On a protected verge at Hargrave it is found with the rare Crested Cow-wheat (*Melampyrum cristatum*). It is also found in chalk pits, several churchyards and cemeteries, old airfields and along a number of disused railways. At Hadleigh, Lavenham and Welnetham old railways have been turned into pleasant walks. Pyramidal Orchids grow close to the old trackside, but without regular management some of these sites are getting overgrown with rank grass and scrub and the orchid will not survive. At Welnetham the management is excellent.

It is unusual today to find Pyramidal Orchid in meadows. It is found in a few Green-winged Orchid sites such as Winks Meadow, Metfield and High House and Martins' Meadows at Monewden. Trist (1960) included it in a list of species associated with Fritillaries (*Fritillaria meleagris*) at Mickfield. At one time it must have been common in the '*chalky pastures*' mentioned by Hind (1889). Sites have been lost in all parts of the County, often due to changes in management or the ploughing up of grasslands. The record from Landguard Common, Felixstowe (Copping, 1990), is one of the few recent instances of its occurrence on (dumped) crag soils. It is scarce in sandy areas, though it can be found in grassland in the Breck where the chalk is near the surface. Like the Bee Orchid it can be a successful coloniser of waste ground on calcareous soils. This is particularly true on the boulder clay where disturbance often creates the sharp drainage required by these species. At a derelict industrial site in Ipswich it grows in some numbers with Bee Orchids, Fairy Flax (*Linum catharticum*), Common Centaury (*Centaurium erythræa*) and Field Scabious (*Knautia arvensis*). Day-flying Six-spot Burnet Moths (*Zygæna filipendulæ*) are frequent at this site; occasionally a moth is found with black pollinia from the Pyramidal Orchids stuck to its proboscis.

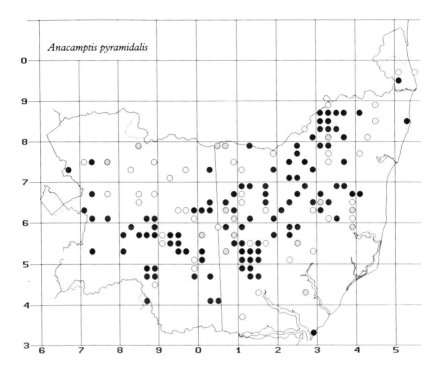

Anacamptis pyramidalis

White-flowered plants have been found at several sites, usually where the species is abundant. These include Great Blakenham, Needham Market, Ipswich, Wattisham and Helmingham. Herbarium specimens of 'albinos' have been collected at Bedingfield (Rev. Alston, 1920 in British Museum) and St. Margaret South Elmham (Anon, 1840 in Cambridge University).

WHITE AND NARROW-LEAVED HELLEBORINE
Cephalanthera ssp.

The two white-flowered helleborines are striking plants of southern Beechwoods on chalk. The White Helleborine (*Cephalanthera damasonium*) is the commoner species. Its tall stems carry several large, grooved, oval leaves and are topped with a loose spike of ivory-white flowers carried close to the stem. It is in flower from late May until the end of June. The Narrow-leaved Helleborine (*C. longifolia*) has more numerous, sword-shaped leaves and pure white flowers in an open spike. It flowers throughout May. The floral bracts provide a clear difference between the two species. In the White Helleborine they are longer than the ovary and in the Narrow-leaved Helleborine they are shorter.

There are old Suffolk records for both White Helleborine and the Narrow-leaved Helleborine.

White Helleborine was recorded by Arthur Mayfield at Mendlesham in 1902 (Simpson, 1982). This record must be viewed with some doubt. The species is mentioned, with the note '*Very rare: one plant only*', in a typed list of flowering plants found at Mendlesham produced by A. Mayfield in 1908. This unpublished list is in the archives of the Ipswich and District Field Club. A later list for the parish published by A. Mayfield in the journal of the Field Club in 1911 (Mayfield, 1911) omits this species, but includes the Greater Butterfly Orchid. I suspect he had changed his original identification and decided the plants were Butterfly Orchid.

The record for Narrow-leaved Helleborine given in Hind (1889) is taken from the Botanist's Guide of 1805. This gives '*about Bury*' by Sir T. G. Cullum. This record was not included by Henslow & Skepper (1860), nor does it appear in Gillingwater (1804) in which there is a list of plants by Sir T. G. Cullum. The latter list does include Butterfly Orchid (*Platanthera bifolia*) '*near Barton Mere*' on Cullum's authority and it is possible this is another case of confusion between two white-flowered orchids.

FROG ORCHID *Cœloglossum viride* (L.) Hartm.

The Frog Orchid is a particularly inconspicuous species often overlooked because of its small size and green flowers. The mid-green basal leaves are broad and strap-shaped. The stem is quite short (5-35 cm) and carries several pointed stem leaves as well as long, leafy bracts. Plants with particularly long bracts have been referred to as var. *bracteata*. The flowers are green, tinged with brown; plants in full sun tend to have more red pigmentation. The tip of the labellum has three lobes, the two outer lobes being much longer than the central one. Flowering occurs between June and August with the main period in early July. It is a widespread but local species in the British Isles and can be found, sometimes in large numbers, in lowland turf on chalk and limestone and in mountain pastures. It will also grow in the damper parts of stabilised sand dunes. In general it prefers short grassland with a basic or neutral soil. Like many orchids it is uncertain in its appearance from year to year.

The discovery in 1990 of a new site for this species in Suffolk after a period of thirty years was perhaps the most exciting record made during the Orchid Survey. About fifteen spikes were found in the corner of an undisturbed meadow on chalky boulder clay at Metfield. The site is a SSSI and has recently been purchased by the Suffolk Wildlife Trust as a reserve (Winks Meadow). It is rich in flora with abundant Green-winged and Pyramidal Orchids and the occasional Common Spotted and Bee Orchid. Other typical plants include Cowslips (*Primula veris*), Adder's Tongue Fern (*Ophioglossum vulgatum*), Pepper Saxifrage (*Silaum silaus*), Spiny Restharrow (*Ononis spinosa*) and Common Quaking Grass (*Briza media*). According to local people the site has never been ploughed and was grazed by sheep before the last war. Frog Orchid is now very scarce in East Anglia; none have been seen in Norfolk or Essex for many years and it is known at only one site in Cambridgeshire.

H. Mendel

Frog Orchid at Winks Meadow, Metfield

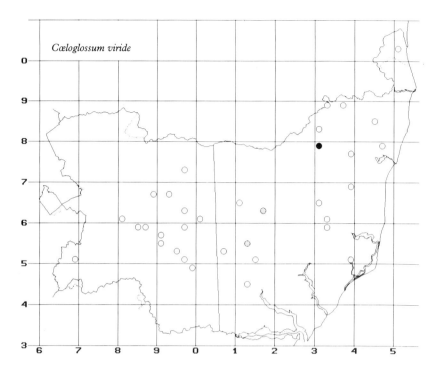

Cœloglossum viride

Until this discovery there had been no records of Frog Orchids for thirty years. The last records, both made in 1960, were from Potash Farm, Debenham where a few plants were found by Mrs. Aldred (Willis, 1960) and from Coddenham by J. E. Lousley (n.b. one of the last records for grassland Fragrant Orchid was also from this parish in 1960). There are very few other twentieth century records. At Hitcham A. L. Bull knew it for some years in a meadow with Fragrant Orchid until the site was ploughed soon after 1950. It was seen during a Suffolk Naturalists' Society field trip to Marlesford Hall in 1954 (Anon, 1954) and it is interesting to note that this was also the site of the first record for Lizard Orchid in 1812. Simpson (1936) recorded it from Naughton, Thorpe Morieux and Barking; at one of these localities it grew with Green-winged and Common Spotted Orchids. He thought it already quite rare and '*hidden away in rough old turfy pastures on a heavy clay soil.*'. Ronald Burn reported var. *bracteata* from Naughton in 1931. There is an undated record from Sotterly made by E. R. Long and another from Mendlesham by A. Mayfield, both probably after 1900.

Simpson (1982) suggests that the old horse pastures which existed on most farms before the introduction of tractors were the main Frog Orchid habitats in Suffolk. Many such pastures were ploughed up between the wars and this appears to have been the fate of several of the sites mentioned above.

However, it was already very rare and I suspect it was not at all common in the 19th century. Hind (1889) recorded the species as *'distributed in all the districts, but not frequent'*, and although it may have been overlooked by some botanists there are relatively few records. Hind's herbarium at Ipswich Museum contains specimens from Little Thurlow, Bury St. Edmunds, Cockfield and Woolpit. Other records extracted from local herbaria include Barton (Lady Blake c.1840), Bradfield (Lathbury, 1834), Rattlesden (Parker, 1881) and Pakenham (Rickards, 1840). The herbarium at Ipswich Museum also has a specimen from a wood near Henley Road, Ipswich taken in 1858 and John Notcutt's specimen from *'the boggy uncultivated part of a field N. W. of Boss Hall* [Ipswich]' collected around 1810. Galpin (1888) has *'abundant in fields near St. Margaret's* [South Elmham]' (E. A. Holmes). Henslow & Skepper (1860) thought it *'frequent'* but cited only a few more parishes (Hawstead, Ickworth, Great Welnetham and Great Glemham). They also repeated records from the Botanist's Guide of 1805 for Mettingham, Yoxford, Bradwell, Halesworth and Harleston. The Rev. G. Crabbe found it in several meadows near Cransford in the 1790s noting that it was *'rare in most of England; but common in this part* [Framlingham area] *of Suffolk'* (Hawes, 1798). Much suitable habitat was destroyed with the increase in arable farming during the early decades of the 19th century. Paget (1834) noted the ploughing of marshes around Yarmouth and thought Frog Orchid already extinct in that area. Gathorne-Hardy (1959) gives a detailed account of an excursion by the Rev. W. Kirby and the Rev. C. Sutton in August 1787, they found Frog Orchid in a *'valuable meadow'* near Chillesford Mill where it grew with Marsh Helleborine.

At many sites, including the meadow at Metfield, Frog Orchid has been found with Green-winged Orchids. Both species are mainly found in old pastures and have survived in the north-east of the county in small fragments of meadow missed by the plough. On the slightly drier boulder clay of the mid-west region Frog Orchid was also found with the chalk grassland form of Fragrant Orchid (*Gymnadenia conopsea* ssp. *conopsea*). Both have been recorded from parishes such as Naughton, Hawstead, Hitcham and Coddenham.

COMMON SPOTTED ORCHID *Dactylorhiza fuchsii* (Druce) Soó

The Common Spotted Orchid is the most common member of the genus *Dactylorhiza*. It is a long-lived plant, often producing a sizeable clump through vegetative multiplication. The basal rosette is quite leafy, each leaf being marked with purple spots. The lowest leaf is the broadest and has a rounded tip; upper leaves are longer and more pointed. The spots are often transversely elongated and can range in size from tiny dots to large blotches covering most of the leaf surface. Flowering occurs any time between mid-May and the end of July; the majority of plants are in flower in mid-June. The flower spikes are long and tapering with many pale lilac flowers. The labellum is wider than long and deeply three-lobed with the lobes roughly equal in size.

R. C. Dryden

Common Spotted Orchid

It is usually marked with a clear double loop pattern made up of dark purple lines and dashes. Petal colour can vary from a deep mauve through to white, though true albinos, which also lack leaf spots and labellum markings, are quite scarce. Summerhayes (1968) describes two distinct races, a tall one in woodland and a shorter one in open grassland. There is considerable variation in the overall size of plants, mainly in response to the amount of available light. The species is widespread in the British Isles. It shows a marked preference for basic soils, but may also be found on neutral clays and gravels.

The Common Spotted Orchid is the most frequent orchid species in Suffolk; it has a very similar distribution to the Twayblade and the two species can often be found growing together. The Common Spotted Orchid can be found on chalk, boulder clay, and rarely, as at Landguard Common (Copping, 1990), on (dumped) Crag. It is now mainly a woodland species in the County. Large numbers grow in many ancient woods and occasionally in secondary woods and more recent plantations. It can survive for many years without flowering, in shady situations, but in most woods it grows along open grassy rides. In ancient woods these rides often support a diverse flora including species such as Oxlip (*Primula elatior*), Wood Spurge (*Euphorbia amygdaloides*), Hairy St John's Wort (*Hypericum hirsutum*) and, occasionally, Greater Butterfly Orchid (*Platanthera chlorantha*). The species is also often found in unimproved grassland on commons and greens, as well as the drier

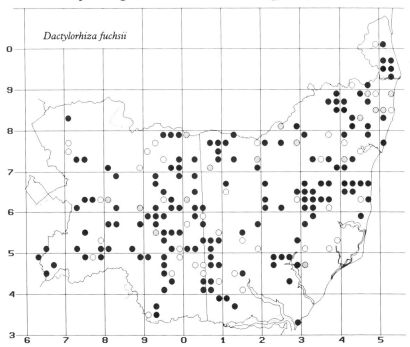

Dactylorhiza fuchsii

parts of fens and marshes. Many such sites were recorded in the Suffolk Wildlife Trust Grassland Survey (Beckett *et al*, 1987). At one time Common Spotted Orchid must have been as frequent in grasslands as it still is in woodlands. It still survives on unimproved common land in parishes like Mellis, Wortham, Stuston and Ilketshall St. Andrew. It is quite frequent on old railway cuttings, especially on chalk, and has colonised several disused airfields in the County. This species is not restricted to ancient sites and, given favourable conditions, can colonise new areas. Other sites include roadside verges at Battisford, Middleton, Theberton and Brockley. A protected verge at Denham has a fine colony, including a range of colour forms from purple to white. Burn (1930) found several variations in shape and colour in the Hadleigh area; the varietal names he ascribed to them are not valid.

As with the Heath Spotted Orchid older records are included under '*Orchis maculata*'. It is possible to re-identify herbarium specimens but, as a common species, it was of little interest to early collectors and is therefore poorly represented in herbaria. As the distribution map shows, sites have been lost throughout the County. There has not been a reduction in range, but it is much less common in grassland habitats than it used to be.

EARLY MARSH ORCHID *Dactylorhiza incarnata* (L.) Soó

This is the most complex and variable of the marsh orchid species. Some of the distinguishing characters described used in floras are not reliable. It is best to use a combination of several characters. The leaves are unspotted, keeled, and often of a bright or even yellow-green colour. The leaf tips are often said to be hooded or 'cucullate' (shaped like the prow of a boat), but Bateman & Denholm (1985) found this character was present in only 40% of plants they examined. Hooded leaves are not found in other marsh orchids. The flowers appear from late May to the end of June, usually a little earlier than the Southern Marsh, but with a considerable overlap. The spikes are cylindrical and often dense, but are rarely as long as those of the Southern Marsh. Floral bracts are long, extending beyond the flowers. Individual flowers are small and typically a pale flesh-pink with upright outer sepals. The labellum is marked with a conspicuous red double loop which encloses a central zone with small dots and dashes. It is similar in shape to the Southern Marsh (i.e. shallowly three-lobed) but with the lateral lobes reflexed giving a narrow, convex appearance. The species is found throughout the British Isles in similar habitats to the Southern Marsh but extending further north. It generally prefers wetter sites with basic ground water. It rarely occurs in large populations; quite often one or two plants can be found at sites with large numbers of Southern Marsh Orchids. In these circumstances it is easy to overlook and it is probably under-recorded. Much suitable habitat has been lost as a result of wetland drainage.

The Early Marsh Orchid is a widespread species in Suffolk with a similar distribution to the Southern Marsh, though it is much less abundant than that species and restricted to wetter, more calcareous sites. The largest populations

Early Marsh Orchid

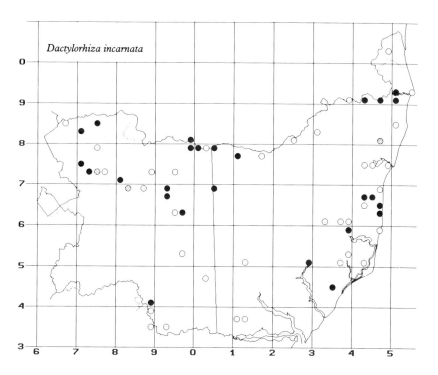

are in fens along the Waveney/ Little Ouse Valley and in Lothingland. It can also be seen in numbers at Pakenham Fen growing in herb-rich grassland with Southern Marsh and abundant Yellow Rattle (*Rhinanthus minor*). Other sites include coastal marshes in the Sizewell area and Breck Fens at Barton Mills and Lakenheath. Few of the records have been identified to subspecies, but it is reasonable to assume that all are for the type (ssp. *incarnata*) unless otherwise stated. Older records are often confused with the Southern Marsh; both species were recorded under *Orchis latifolia* in the 19th century and identification of herbarium specimens is very difficult. The earliest record I have found is a specimen at the British Museum collected by the Rev. W. Kirby from Oakley Park (near Hoxne) in 1832. It has undergone a sharper decline than the Southern Marsh, having been lost from many sites where that species still survives.

In May 1990 Rev. R. A. Addington discovered a most unusual specimen of Early Marsh Orchid in a marshy meadow at Finningham. This appeared to be a 'pseudopeloric' mutant (see Bateman, 1985) in which the labellum had no spur and was shaped like the other petals.

A number of colour forms of Early Marsh Orchid have been described, (see Bateman & Denholm, 1985). In Suffolk ssp. *pulchella* and ssp. *ochroleuca* have been recorded, as well as the typical form (ssp. *incarnata*).

F. W. Simpson

I. A. Denholm

Early Marsh Orchid ssp. *pulchella*   Early Marsh Orchid ssp. *ochroleuca*

Ssp. *pulchella* has intense purple-violet flowers and bracts suffused with purple anthocyanin pigment. Unlike other subspecies it can tolerate acid soils and may even be found in *Sphagnum* bogs. It is found throughout the range of the species, often with ssp. *incarnata*, though it can be the dominant form in more acid areas.

Ssp. *pulchella* has been found at several sites in the County, not always on acid substrates. It was recorded at Thelnetham Fen by H. W. Pugsley in 1938 and was found there by P. J. O. Trist in 1965. F. W. Simpson found it at Redgrave Fen in the 1930s. Dr. I. A. Denholm also found it at Redgrave with ssp. *incarnata* in 1988. David Lang found a single plant at Eastbridge in 1971 amongst more than a hundred ssp. *incarnata*. It used to be found in several of the Breck Fens before drainage lowered the water table. W. C. Barton collected specimens of both ssp. *pulchella* and ssp. *incarnata* from a marsh at Mildenhall in 1916. Dr. I. A. Denholm found it at Lakenheath Fen in 1980, in habitat '*more suitable for subsp. incarnata*'. The first record of *D. incarnata* from Suffolk is in Hind (1889); Dr. White (of Lavenham) found it in 1860 in '*old pastures around Felsham Hall Wood*'. Dr. White also recorded Heath Spotted Orchid from the same area, which suggests the habitat was acid. His Early Marsh plants may well have been ssp. *pulchella*.

Ssp. *ochroleuca* is the most distinct subspecies and some have suggested it merits specific rank. It lacks anthocyanin pigments and has pale, straw yellow flowers. It is a stout plant with a tall broad stem and large leaves. The spikes are lax with long bracts extending well beyond the flowers. The labellum is large, unmarked and deeply three-lobed (not unlike the Common Spotted Orchid in shape). It is restricted to calcareous fens in East Anglia, and was first found at Roydon Fen in Norfolk by J. E. Lousley in 1936. The largest populations occurred in fens in the Waveney Valley, but since these are progressively drying out as the water table falls, it is now endangered in Britain (Bateman & Denholm, 1985). This subspecies should not be identified on flower colour alone. Partial albinos (lacking anthocyanins) of other Early Marsh subspecies (especially ssp.s *incarnata* and *pulchella*) are not infrequent and can also have cream or off-white flowers. They do not have the distinct size and shape (particularly the three-lobed labellum) of ssp. *ochroleuca*.

Ssp. *ochroleuca* is one of the most elusive and intriguing of Suffolk's orchids. Some records are undoubtedly the result of confusion with albino variants of ssp.s *incarnata* and *pulchella*. I photographed a variant of this type at Redgrave Fen in 1985 (conf. Dr. I. A. Denholm), growing alongside several normal plants. There are two herbarium specimens taken at Thelnetham Fen in 1883. One, which I think is correctly identified, is labelled 'v. *ochroleuca*' and was collected by the Rev. J. D. Gray; it is now in Cambridge University herbarium. The other, with the label '*white and mottled flowers*', was collected by the Rev. W. M. Hind and is now in the herbarium at Ipswich Museum; this specimen is probably an albino ssp. *incarnata*. H. W. Pugsley recorded ssp. *ochroleuca* at Thelnetham in 1938. In addition to the record in Simpson (1982) for Coney Weston; it was seen at Market Weston Fen by P. A. Wright in 1971; it has not been seen at this site since then. At Redgrave it was recorded by F. W. Simpson in 1971 and again in 1980. Having seen the albino mentioned above at Redgrave I was a little doubtful about this site. However, Arthur Rivett of the Suffolk Wildlife Trust has shown me slides taken in another part of the fen in 1987 which were definitely ssp. *ochroleuca*. The plant(s) at Redgrave are very probably the last remaining in Suffolk.

HEATH SPOTTED ORCHID *Dactylorhiza maculata* (L.) Soó ssp. *ericetorum* (Linton) P. F. Hunt & Summerhayes

The Heath Spotted Orchid is a dainty, attractive species. It is much confused with the similar Common Spotted Orchid (*D. fuchsii*) and needs close examination for positive identification. The leaves are narrower and more pointed than the Common Spotted and the spots are usually small and round; leaf spots may vary a lot and in any large population some plants with heavily spotted leaves can be found. The flowers appear from mid-June to mid-July, slightly later than the Common Spotted but with a considerable overlap when both species are in flower. The spike is short and conical particularly when the first flowers are opening. Plants on drier soils and in exposed situations will often be quite small with spikes only about 2-3 cm long. Flowers have a base colour of palest pink to white, though occasional darker forms can be found. The spur is shorter or equal in length to the ovary and much more slender than in the Common Spotted. The labellum shape is the best character to separate

Heath Spotted Orchid

the two species. In the Heath Spotted the labellum is broad with two rounded outer lobes often with a frilled edge. The triangular central lobe is much smaller and is shorter than or equal in length to the outer lobes. The Common Spotted has three triangular labellum lobes which are equal in size and do not have a frilled edge. Labellum markings in the Heath Spotted vary from minute, red dots and dashes to strong lines and loops. They do not form the characteristic double loop of the Common Spotted. The two species were recognised as distinct in 1915 by the Rev. E. F. Linton, who recorded the Heath Spotted from Suffolk at Polstead (Willis, 1959). All earlier records were lumped under the name '*Orchis maculata*'.

In Britain the Heath Spotted Orchid is most common in the North and West in mountainous areas with high rainfall. It has a similar distribution pattern to that of Heath Rush (*Juncus squarrosus*) and Heath Lousewort (*Pedicularis sylvatica*). All of these species were more common in the South and East before the drainage of so many lowland bogs. In Suffolk the two species of spotted orchid are very rarely found close together; the Heath Spotted is a plant of old pastures and wet heaths on acid soils and the Common Spotted is usually found in woods and always on alkaline soils.

Most 19th Century Suffolk herbarium specimens labelled as '*maculata*' are the Common Spotted Orchid and there are few records of the Heath Spotted before 1950. However, it seems likely this species was once much more frequent both in pastures and heathy bogs. Simpson (1935) recorded

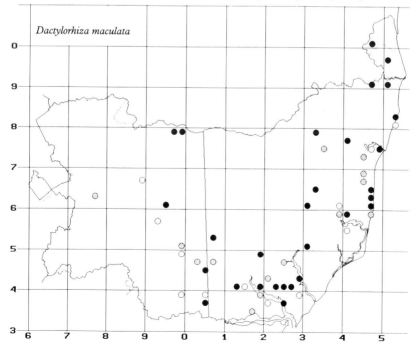

it under the name '*Orchis elodes*', as '*common in heathy bogs*'. Henslow & Skepper (1860) note that Dr. White found '*an unusual and very handsome variety* [of Spotted Orchid] *in old pastures round Felsham Hall wood, flowering a little later than the common form*'. This was certainly the Heath Spotted Orchid. At a few sites the Heath Spotted can still be found in large numbers with quite a lot of variation in leaf spots, flower colour and markings and in the size of individual plants. True albinos with unspotted leaves, white, unmarked flowers and white pollen masses can occasionally be found at such sites, as can plants in which all the flowers are upside down.

Simpson (1982) reports its extinction from several 10km squares and this trend has continued. Many grassland sites have been ploughed and reseeded – a process which destroys the underground tubers and from which it never recovers. Some of the best sites are now on the Felixstowe peninsula including a superb meadow at Trimley and a few marshes around Nacton, Kirton and Falkenham. The complete absence of records from the Breck is surprising. Small pockets of ancient grassland in Lothingland still contain this species and it also occurs in old acid pastures at Benacre and Barnby (Hyde & Simpson, 1987). In a remote corner in Tuddenham St. Martin it can be found with the rare Betony (*Stachys officinalis*). Heathlands suffered badly during the Enclosure period when many commons and 'waste lands' were ploughed up. Paget (1834) records the loss of commons in the Yarmouth area and describes the local heaths as '*little more than a continuous surface of furze and heath, whose interstices are filled up with the rein-deer lichen, and various species of* Hypnum; *the soil of which they consist, is, after these shrubs are cut down, generally found to repay the expense of cultivation*'. Drainage has also badly affected this species. Wet acid soils do not produce the rich grazing of alkaline wet meadows and are therefore much more likely to be 'improved'. The drainage of the larger acid bogs in north west and north east Suffolk in the early 19th century (see Bog Orchid) must also have destroyed many suitable sites. More subtle changes, such as reduction in grazing pressure, can result in heathlands reverting back to woodland. Sites such as Wolves Wood near Hadleigh have retained a few heathland species in the more open glades.

SOUTHERN MARSH ORCHID
Dactylorhiza praetermissa (Druce) Soó

This species is by far the commonest of the marsh orchids to be found in southern Britain. It is usually larger in all parts than the Early Marsh or the Narrow-leaved Marsh and, although variable, it is not difficult to identify. The Southern Marsh Orchid is a stout, leafy plant with hollow stems which can reach 70 cm in large specimens. The basal leaves are bright green, flat and quite broad (usually more than 2 cm), the widest point being at or below the middle of the leaf. The stem carries a number of sheathing leaves which merge with the long floral bracts. The cylindrical flower spikes are often large and are quite tightly packed with flowers. Individual flowers are also larger than those of other marsh orchids and are distinct in having a broad, often concave, labellum. The outer sepals are almost vertical when the flowers are fully open.

Southern Marsh Orchid and Common
Milkwort at Barton Mills

Leopard Marsh Orchid (see p. 53)

The labellum can be entire or shallowly three-lobed with the central lobe slightly longer than the laterals. Markings are mainly concentrated in the central part of the labellum; they consist of small dots and dashes and do not form the loop patterns seen in the Early Marsh. Flower colour is quite variable; usually it is pale mauve but in most populations individuals can be found with quite deep purple or magenta blooms. Albinos are very rare. Flowering occurs later than with the other marsh orchids; the main period is from mid-June to early August.

The Southern Marsh is a widespread species in southern England. It can be found in a variety of wetland habitats including fens, marshes and wet meadows and occasionally on drier chalk substrates. Like many orchids it shows a strong preference for sites where the soil (or the ground water) is base-rich. In many cases this orchid is accompanied by Ragged Robin (*Lychnis flos-cuculi*). In the field the pink flowers of the Ragged Robin can be seen from a distance, providing a good indication of possible orchid sites.

The Southern Marsh Orchid is still quite frequent in Suffolk; large populations can be found in wet marshes along the coastal strip and in fens and marshes in the valleys of the Waveney, Ouse and Lark. Smaller colonies occur in scattered wet meadows throughout the County. Many sites have been lost and others are under threat from drainage and a general lowering of the water table. A fine colony can be seen by the entrance to the picnic site at Wilford Bridge, Melton. In wet meadows by the River Lark at Barton Mills a beautiful dark colour form grows in profusion with the Common Milkwort (*Polygala vulgaris*) – an association I have not seen elsewhere. The distribution map shows considerable recorder bias in the area east of Ipswich, mainly as a result of my own fieldwork. However, this area does have a lot of suitable habitat, crag soils provide base rich ground water and there has been less extensive drainage than in other parts of the County. It is scarce in the south-west and uncommon on the mid-Suffolk boulder clays. It does not occur in many of the old pastures favoured by the Green-winged Orchid.

A relatively dwarf form grows on dry chalk grassland, and is rare. In 1978 J. C. Rose called E. Milne-Redhead's attention to a large population of this form colonising the dry bottom of a deep chalk-pit at Bramford. As the pit had been scheduled for infilling, the Suffolk Wildlife Trust got permission to move the plants to a safer site. On 14th & 15th July 1979, a very hot day, several hundred plants of the Southern Marsh and some Pyramidal Orchids were dug up and replanted in a new site nearby, on a part of the pit already infilled and covered with chalk. Ten years later they were flowering and increasing. Similar plants have been found in a chalk pit at Worlington by Mrs E. M. Hyde in 1989.

The species is not restricted to undisturbed sites; in a few places it has been able to colonise new areas in a surprisingly short time. At the Sizewell Power Station site large areas of reed bed were buried under dumped sand (including shelly Norwich Crag) between 1965 and 1970. This area was

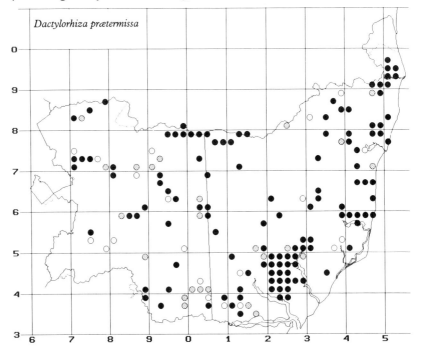

Dactylorhiza prætermissa

rapidly colonised and within 14 years supported dense stands of marsh orchids with as many as 60 plants per square metre in places. Some of this area was damaged during construction of Sizewell 'B' and plants (including several hybrids) were transferred to the University of East Anglia at Norwich. It is planned to reintroduce these plants when disturbance at the site has ceased. The species has been able to colonise a number of industrial waste sites in Britain.

Hermy & Vanhecke (1990) have shown clear correlations between the numbers of flower spikes in Southern Marsh Orchid and the height of the water table in winter. Long winter inundations (over one month) can cause severe declines or even the complete loss of plants from an area. This may not be irreversible where recolonisation from nearby sites, which are not flooded, is possible.

A striking variety of the Southern Marsh with ring-spotted leaves has been referred to as the Leopard Marsh or var. *pardalina* (var. *junialis* in Bateman & Denholm, 1983). It resembles the normal form in size and shape, but has distinctive, predominantly annular leaf spots and bolder, more looped labellum markings. It has often been confused with hybrids between Southern Marsh and the Spotted Orchids (Sanford, 1988). Several writers (Bateman & Denholm 1983, Lang 1980, Summerhayes 1968) have clearly described this variety, but it does not feature in the more popular illustrated guides.

M. N. Sanford

Range of leaf spotting from typical Southern Marsh to Leopard Marsh in a population at Brightwell

The variety *pardalina* can be found throughout the range of the species in Suffolk. In the valley of the Mill River at Brightwell there are several superb meadows in which it is the dominant form. Some plants have leaf spots so large and dense that the whole leaf appears purplish black. These specimens also have strongly coloured flowers in which the central part of the labellum is entirely dark purple with a paler margin. A whole range of intermediates between var. *pardalina* and the normal unspotted form can be found. At Bromeswell Green and Nacton Water Meadows, reserves managed by the Suffolk Wildlife Trust, spotted and unspotted forms can be found in roughly equal proportions. Other sites where I have seen var. *pardalina* in small numbers include Barton Mills, Market Weston, Barnby, Eastbridge, Foxhall, Melton and Redisham. Mrs G. Crompton has also found this variety at Worlington Golf Course.

Albino plants are very rare and have only been seen recently at Eastbridge (E. Milne-Redhead, 1980) and Westleton (Mrs E. M. Hyde, 1976). There is a specimen from Cornard taken in 1844 in the herbarium at Ipswich Museum.

NARROW-LEAVED MARSH ORCHID
Dactylorhiza traunsteineri (Saut.) Soó

The Narrow-leaved Marsh Orchid is a small and little known species. Its small stature means it can easily be overlooked or mistaken for other marsh orchids. It is a rather slender plant with a flexuous stem up to 30 cm tall. The leaves, which rarely number more than five, are narrow and almost grasslike. They are usually less than 1.5 cm wide and 12 cm long and unspotted. Occasionally plants have small transversely elongated, solid spots concentrated towards the leaf tips. The flowers are produced from late May to early June, a little earlier than other marsh orchids. The spikes are perhaps the most characteristic feature of the species. The inflorescence is short (rarely more than 7 cm) with rather pale, lilac flowers arranged in a lax spike. There are usually less than twenty flowers to a spike. The bracts are long, projecting well beyond the flowers. The labellum is three-lobed with the central lobe longer (often by more than 1 mm) than the reflexed lateral lobes. It is diamond shaped (deltoid) and evenly marked with dashes and loops which do not form the patterns often seen in other dactylorchid species.

It is almost entirely restricted to calcareous fens and has very similar ecological requirements to the Fen Orchid. It prefers the wettest parts of fens and often grows in the mossy layer at the edges of reed beds. The species has a scattered distribution in Britain, but is rapidly decreasing as drainage and reclamation destroy much of its habitat. Summerhayes (1968) suggests that it may once have been more widespread and abundant. It is still found in Ireland, and in fens in Anglesey, Berkshire, Hampshire, Yorkshire and East Anglia.

This orchid was only described as a separate species of Marsh Orchid in the 1930s. There is still much debate as to its precise status, particularly whether British plants are conspecific with those from classic alpine localities.

F. W. Simpson

Narrow-leaved Marsh Orchid

It appears to me to be quite distinct as a species and I do not agree with Bateman & Denholm (1983), who suggest that British plants are a subspecies of the widespread European *D. majalis* (see Foley 1990b and Roberts, 1988).

There are very few records of this species from Suffolk. This is mainly due to its relative scarcity, but may also be partly due to the very small number of recorders able to recognise it. Bellamy & Rose (1960) were amongst the first to record its presence in this County. During their survey of the Waveney-Ouse valley fens they found it at Market Weston, Thelnetham and Redgrave Fens. It was also seen at Thelnetham by E. L. Swann in 1967. Simpson (1982) includes an undated record for Hinderclay. The only 19th century specimen I have found is in the Cambridge University herbarium. It was collected by the Rev. J. D. Gray at Thelnetham Fen in 1885 and is labelled '*Orchis incarnata* var. *angustifolia*'. It is almost certainly *D. traunsteineri* and, if so, is the earliest record of this species from Suffolk. Hind (1889) includes records for '*Orchis angustifolia*' from Hopton and Redgrave Fens. It has survived at Redgrave and Lopham Fens, but the only plants I have seen are in South Lopham on the Norfolk side of the border (also recorded here by D. Lang, 1967 and Dr. I. A. Denholm, 1984). The record from Hitcham in Bull (1977) is probably in error for Southern Marsh. Marsh Orchid specimens from Hitcham in Henslow's herbarium are all Southern Marsh.

The only record outside the Waveney-Ouse valley is from a marshy meadow at Eastbridge, near the Minsmere bird reserve, where it was found

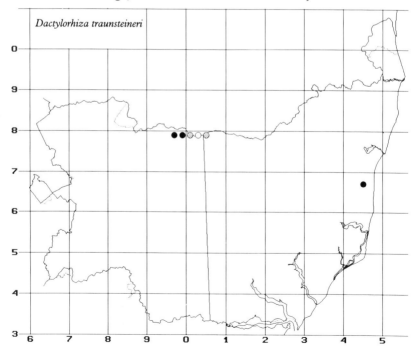

by D. Wells and E. Milne-Redhead in June 1982. Southern Marsh Orchid is also present at this site and Early Marsh grows in meadows nearby. These wet grazing meadows contain a species-rich sward including a variety of *Carex* species and several scarce herbs.

The only other recent records are from Market Weston and Coney Weston Fens, where it has been seen by a number of recorders. It grows there on the edges of *Phragmites* fen. David Lang has suggested (Lang, 1980 and in correspondence) that *D. prætermissa* is 'hybridising out' *traunsteineri* in Market Weston Fen. In 1967 he observed 30 plants of *traunsteineri* and several hybrids with *prætermissa* at the north end of the fen. By 1971 only 5 *traunsteineri* could be found and there were more than 100 plants of the hybrid. He suggests that the hybrids are more robust and better suited to drier conditions. It is worth noting that Bellamy & Rose (1960) did not record any hybrids present in 1960. Dr. I. A. Denholm examined plants at Market Weston in the 1980s and found '*a morphological continuum from typical* praetermissa *to plants that approach, but don't quite reach,* traunsteineri'. He has noticed such continua at other East Anglian sites including Foulden Common, Norfolk and Chippenham Fen, Cambridgeshire. I have had a report (C. Hawke pers. comm. 1989) that *traunsteineri* is still to be found in Market Weston Fen, but have not seen specimens.

BROAD-LEAVED HELLEBORINE
Epipactis helleborine (L.) Crantz

The Broad-leaved Helleborine is a large robust species often growing to nearly a metre in height. Like the Violet Helleborine it has a deep-seated rootstock which enables it to persist even where paths have been laid on top of it. Despite its size it is quite difficult to spot, having rather dull flowers and often growing in heavy shade. Sometimes several stems arise from one plant, but it does not form large clumps like the Violet Helleborine. The leaves are dark green and oval in shape, the many ribs giving a pleated look. The tall flower spikes can be found between mid-July and September; height and flower colour are very variable depending to a large extent on available light. Plants in deep shade are more spindly with paler flowers while plants exposed to more light will be shorter with flowers flushed with red or pink. The sepals are green, sometimes tinged pink at the tips. The labellum is made up of a reddish brown cup (hypochile) and a pinkish brown lip (epichile) which usually has a reflexed tip.

This species is by far the commonest member of the genus *Epipactis*; it is widely distributed throughout the British Isles and can be found in a variety of different habitats ranging from roadside verges to limestone pavements and from acid to alkaline soils. Individual sites rarely contain more than one or two plants It is a surprisingly scarce plant in East Anglia. Although mainly found in ancient woodland it is quite capable of colonising secondary woodland and plantations and has been found in large numbers at a few sites in quite recent conifer plantations.

I. J. Killeen

M. N. Sanford

Broad-leaved Helleborine

The first Suffolk (and British) record is cited as that of Dr. William Turner in 1562. His record of the '*Satyrion of Dioscorides*' in the second part of his New Herball gives the locality as '*pastures at Digswell in Suffolk*'. However, Digswell is in Hertfordshire which casts some doubt on this record. An early specimen is in the herbarium of the Rev. W. Kirby, found by Mrs. Davy in 1796 in '*the plantation near the Lodges*' at Heveningham. It is interesting that this record is from a plantation; Lodge Wood is marked on Hodskinson's 1783 map of Suffolk and had probably been a plantation (perhaps on the site of an older wood) for around forty years by the time Mrs. Davy found her plant. The wood is still there, virtually unchanged in outline, but there have been no recent records of Helleborines. Most Suffolk records are from the belt of ancient woods on chalky boulder clay in the middle of the County; here the species is associated with shady coppice of Hazel or Hornbeam. At Offton it grows in a small wood along with Greater Butterfly, Bird's-nest, Early Purple, Common Spotted and Twayblade; there is a specimen taken in 1858 from this site in Cambridge University herbarium. With the cessation of coppicing many of these woods have deteriorated, very few records from ancient woods were made during the survey period and the species appears to have been lost from several such sites, including a number of SSSIs, within the last ten years. Other sites include secondary woodland and plantations, often where there is heavy shade. I have seen it under the dense canopy of young Sycamores and amongst conifers. At The Grove in

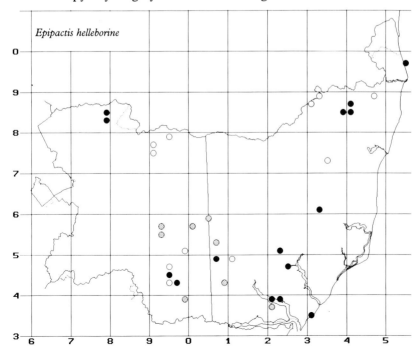

Epipactis helleborine

Felixstowe it grew in mixed Oak woodland for over forty years until new gravel paths were laid on top of the site – I hope if it reappears paths can be re-routed to avoid further damage. In the Breck it appeared in Forestry Commission conifer plantations during the 1960s and quite large numbers have recently been found at Brandon and Santon Downham. One plant with double flowers was noticed by members of Thetford Natural History Society at Santon Downham in 1987. Although there are likely to be new sites appearing in the County for this species, the recent decline in ancient woodlands is disturbing. The precise requirements of both Broad-leaved and Violet Helleborines need detailed investigation if they are to be retained in woodland reserves.

MARSH HELLEBORINE *Epipactis palustris* (L.) Crantz

The Marsh Helleborine is a rare and attractive species. Although the stems are short, the relatively large flowers make it visible from some distance. It is the only helleborine to be found in wetland habitats and unlike other *Epipactis* species it has a creeping rhizomatous root system. It is not found in shady places and appears to have little dependence on mycorrhizal fungi. The leaves are mid-green and lanceolate in shape forming rosettes in non-flowering shoots. The flowering spikes are produced in July and August and are usually less than 50 cm tall with ten to twenty flowers loosely distributed on one side of the spike. The pointed outer sepals are green suffused with pink or purple, the inner petals are white. The broad white labellum is the most striking feature; it is frilled at the edges with a bright yellow plate at the top. It increases vegetatively by the growth of new shoots from the branching rhizome and can spread rather like Lily of the Valley to cover quite a large area. It is found in fens with basic water and in damp hollows on calcareous sand dunes. Plants in fens tend to be taller than those on dunes, though this is probably due to environmental factors rather than any genetic differences. Many of the fen habitats have been lost in Britain due to drainage, and Marsh Helleborine is now only found in large numbers in coastal dunes in the South and East of England and West Wales and some of the better Norfolk fens. The variety *ochroleuca* has yellowish white flowers and occurs throughout the range of the species; it has not been recorded from Suffolk, but has been seen at several sites in Norfolk.

In Suffolk the species is now very rare and restricted to three or four sites, all in calcareous fens in the Waveney/Little Ouse Valley. Several of these sites are not stable and are in danger of drying out as drainage of the surrounding farmland lowers the water table. It was never a common plant in the County, but had a much wider distribution before the major 19th Century drainage projects. In the Lark Valley it was common in bogs at Tuddenham and Lackford. Lady Blake collected a number of herbarium specimens from Lackford Bridge around 1840. It was still at Icklingham in 1965, but there have been no subsequent records. At one time Marsh Helleborine could also be found in the Stour Valley; the first Suffolk record was made by J. Andrews of Sudbury in 1745. It used to be found in the Nayland area in the 1930s and at Cornard, probably the Mere, in the 1950s.

M. N. Sanford

A. J. Cooper

Marsh Helleborine

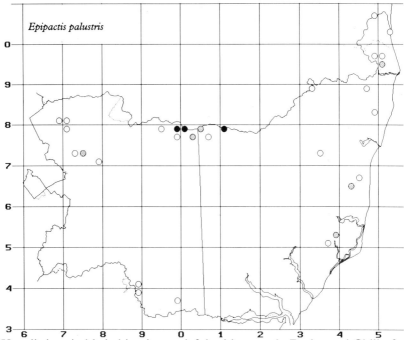

Epipactis palustris

Very little suitable habitat is now left in this area. At Butley and Chillesford it grew in marshes fed by water draining through calcareous crag deposits. Here it was found (and roots collected) by Sutton and Kirby during their excursion through East Suffolk in August 1787 (Gathorne-Hardy, 1959; Simpson, 1960). It was refound at Chillesford in 1960 by N. Kerr, but was probably lost soon after that date when the habitat was destroyed. Similar marshes at Eastbridge and Theberton also lost this species around 1960. It was found at Wrentham in 1921 and a few plants were recorded from Heveningham in 1945 (Burton, 1945).

Of the remaining sites, Market Weston Fen is probably the best. Here it grows in some numbers in a superb mixed herb community with Fragrant Orchid (*Gymnadenia conopsea* ssp. *densiflora*), Marsh Lousewort (*Pedicularis palustris*) and Blunt-flowered Rush (*Juncus subnodulosus*). The perennial growth of this species enables it to remain in suitable sites for a very long time. The fen is fed by a number of springs and is still very wet, probably not very different from when the Rev. J. D. Gray collected specimens there in 1884.

This sort of community is very fragile; the shallow rhizomes of the helleborine are easily trampled and broken. The level of the water table and the nutrient content of the water are vitally important with even small fluctuations having serious effects. The decline of this species is paralleled by that of the Fragrant Orchid and the now extinct Fen Orchid. Unless great efforts are made to prevent the remaining sites drying out this species may also disappear before the end of the century.

GREEN-FLOWERED HELLEBORINE
Epipactis phyllanthes G. E. Sm.

The Green, or Pendulous-flowered Helleborine is like a smaller version of the Broad-leaved Helleborine. The flowers are produced in July and August in narrow spikes; they differ from other woodland helleborines in lacking any red or purple pigmentation. They do not open fully and those at the top of the spike often remain as closed buds. Typically these flowers are self-fertilised even in the unopened (cleistogamous) flowers. As there is no out-breeding, populations in different parts of Britain maintain slightly different characteristics. In the past these variations were given specific status (*E. vectensis, pendula* & *cambrensis*) but work by Dr. D. P. Young in the 1950s showed that they were all forms of one species. The species is found in similar habitats to the Broad-leaved Helleborine; sometimes the two species are found growing together. It is likely that the Green-flowered Helleborine has been under-recorded due to confusion with the Broad-leaved.

There is only a single record of this species from Suffolk. Green-flowered Helleborine was found by Dr. E. F. Warburg (of British Flora fame) in the grounds of Melton Hall in 1952. It was identified as this species by Dr. D. P. Young (see above). This site was destroyed in the 1970s (pers. comm. E. Milne-Redhead).

In 1984 it was found in some numbers at Snailwell in Cambridgeshire right on the edge of the County boundary. The only record of Green-flowered Helleborine from Norfolk was just over the County border at Santon in 1969; its identity was again confirmed by Dr. Young. The Broad-leaved Helleborine occurs in large numbers on the Suffolk side of the border at Brandon and it is quite possible the Green-flowered Helleborine could be found among these plants.

VIOLET HELLEBORINE *Epipactis purpurata* Sm.

The Violet Helleborine is a scarce and little known species. It is quite similar to the Broad-leaved Helleborine and the two species occasionally occur together. These two species differ in leaf colour and width, with the Violet Helleborine having narrower more lanceolate leaves, which are greyish and often flushed with purple. When growing in the same locality the Violet Helleborine will usually be smaller and more slender than the Broad-leaved. It also tends to grow in clumps of as many as twenty spikes rather than the single stems of the Broad-leaved, and it flowers from early August to September, somewhat later than the Broad-leaved, although the flowering periods overlap for about a month. The flowers are similar in shape, but have more pointed sepals and a pale pink labellum lip where the Broad-leaved has a pinkish brown lip. The ovaries are rough with short hairs. It can tolerate much heavier shade and more acidic soils than the Broad-leaved and is not dependent on mycorrhizal fungi. In Britain it has a much smaller range than the Broad-leaved being restricted to Southern and South-eastern England.

64

Violet Helleborine

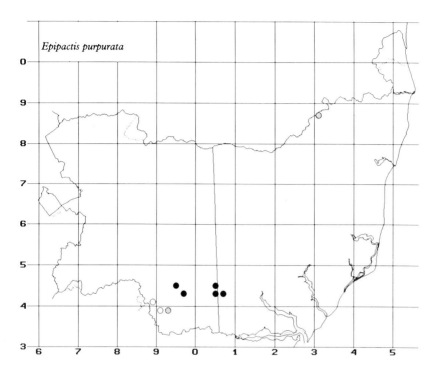

Violet Helleborine was first described in Smith's English Flora (1825), but was confused with other helleborines for many years. It was not noticed in Suffolk until 1912. A specimen collected by B. T. Lowne at that time from Grays Wood, Cornard is in the Kew Herbarium. The species was still present at the same site in 1956, when it was 'refound' by Dr. D. P. Young (Trist, 1956), but the wood has suffered much clearance since then and Violet Helleborine is most unlikely to have survived. In Norfolk the species was found much earlier with four sites listed in the Rev. Kirby Trimmer's 1866 Flora. It is interesting to note that the last record for that county was in 1910, two years before the first Suffolk record.

With so few early records it is difficult to say much about its past distribution. From the few records available it appears to have been lost from a number of ancient woods, but to have maintained its range. This is similar to the situation nationally. In Suffolk it is restricted to ancient woods with heavy shade and basic to neutral soils. It is not found in the more recent plantations that the Broad-leaved Helleborine has colonised. Few of these plantations provide the combination of shade and soil type required. It seems very unlikely that seeds would reach new sites from the small number of very sheltered localities remaining in the County. Bateman (1981) reports that it is the only species of orchid to be increasing in Hertfordshire, possibly due to the neglect of coppices leading to a reduction in light intensity at ground level.

All extant colonies in the County are protected as SSSIs and with careful management the species should maintain its numbers and perhaps increase at such sites. In some places grazing deer can damage flowering stems and the plants are caged. In Groton Wood it grows sparingly under neglected lime coppice in the ancient part of the wood and much more plentifully in hazel coppice under standard oak and ash in parts of the secondary wood known to have been agricultural land in the distant past. At Wolves Wood near Hadleigh it grows under the very deep shade of old hornbeam coppice. There is little competition from other plants as they are unable to grow in such low light levels. The soil is sticky boulder clay with only a relatively thin leaf litter. Plants vary in size from year to year with only single spikes put up in dry years and larger clumps appearing in more favourable conditions.

CREEPING LADY'S TRESSES *Goodyera repens* (L.) R. Br.

This small, slightly hairy species is one of the few orchids that will grow in the acid soils of pine forests. It is a native of the ancient Caledonian forests of Scotland where it grows in deep, moist litter of rotting needles and moss. Creeping Lady's Tresses flowers in July and August; the short stems have sweet- scented, creamy white flowers in a single spiral row, though the actual flowers tend to all face in one direction. There are several conifer plantations in North Norfolk where this species has become naturalised; it was first recorded in Norfolk in 1885. As it was not recorded before this date it seems likely it was introduced to these sites with soil around seedling Pines which were being brought from Scotland in large numbers. Petch & Swann (1968) also record introductions near Brandon, but it is not known if these were successful. Certainly it is worth looking out for in any of the forestry plantations in the north-west of the County.

The only Suffolk record for this species is from East Suffolk at Stuston Common. This also appears to be the most southerly record in the British Isles. It was found in 1932 by L. Green (1934) and wrongly assigned to Norfolk. It was recorded at the same site in 1935 by A. Mayfield. I have been unable to trace any further details of this record. There are no conifer plantations in Stuston and the record may have been from a plant introduced to a garden. Mayfield was a very competent botanist and there is no reason to doubt the identification.

FRAGRANT ORCHID *Gymnadenia conopsea* (L.) R. Br.

The Fragrant Orchid is a beautiful species with tall elegant flower spikes and a delicious scent which is sweet but not sickly. The leaves are long, narrow and folded. The flower spikes are long and densely packed with small, bright pink flowers. The labellum is short and three-lobed with a long, slender, curved spur. White-flowered plants are occasionally encountered. There are three subspecies found in Britain which are distinguished by several minor characters which have been quantified by Francis Rose in Rich & Rich (1988). Ssp. *borealis* is restricted to northern Britain and needs no further description here.

M. N. Sanford

Fragrant Orchid ssp. *densiflora*

Ssp. *densiflora* is found in calcareous marshes and fens. It is tall (30-60 cm) with very sweet-smelling flowers; the scent has often been compared to that of carnations. The flowers appear from early July to August and are not always as densely packed as the name would suggest. The labellum is shallowly three-lobed with distinct 'shoulders' at the sides; the lateral sepals are truncate at the tips and are held horizontally. Ssp. *conopsea* is mainly found in dry chalk grassland and is quite frequent on downland pastures. The plants are shorter (20-40 cm) with slightly smaller flowers which appear from early June to mid-July. The scent is sweet, but with an acid or 'rancid' background. The labellum is more deeply three-lobed and lacks the 'shoulders' of ssp. *densiflora*. The lateral sepals are pointed at the tips and turn downwards at an angle of about 30 degrees from horizontal. Both of the southern subspecies are quite widespread in Britain, but are generally rather local in their occurrence. Ssp. *densiflora* is the characteristic plant of East Anglian fens.

The only authenticated record of ssp. *conopsea* in Suffolk is from Hitcham. A. L. Bull knew it at two old meadows south of Home Wood, Hitcham, where it grew with Frog Orchid; both were last seen there in 1950. There were almost 8 acres *'with scarce room to put one's feet without treading on them'*; it must have been a magnificent sight. The Rev. Henslow collected a herbarium specimen of *G. conopsea* at Hitcham in 1850. The record from Coddenham in 1960 by M. Bendix (Willis, 1961) is without details of the subspecies, but there was suitable habitat for ssp. *conopsea* in the parish. In the late 1970s a Fragrant Orchid was seen at Martins' Meadows at Monewden. The subspecies was not determined and it has not been seen since that time. Ssp. *conopsea* can still be found on the Devil's Dyke on Newmarket Heath in Cambridgeshire, less than a mile from Suffolk.

Subspecific status is not recorded for any of the 19th century records and it is very difficult to determine from herbarium specimens. There is a specimen in Kirby's herbarium at Ipswich Museum collected in 1796 at Bath Hills near Bungay, just in Norfolk, which may well be this subspecies. Another possible specimen at Ipswich was collected by J. Atkins from Burstall, near Ipswich in 1908. Sites referred to in Henslow & Skepper (1860) may have had suitable habitat for ssp. *conopsea*. These included damp pastures at Hardwick, Hawstead, Naughton, Bungay, Framlingham and Henslow's site at Hitcham. Records for that Flora relied heavily on previously published sources and local herbaria and it is safe to assume the species was more widespread than this list might suggest. Ssp. *conopsea* is now extinct in Suffolk; apart from the remarkable meadows at Hitcham it appears many sites had been lost well before the turn of the century. The ploughing up of grazing meadows for arable use during the early 19th century must have had a serious effect and it was probably very rare by the time Hind published his Flora in 1889.

Ssp. *densiflora* is still found in Suffolk, though it is now restricted to about five sites, all on calcareous fens. It survives in reserves at Redgrave, Thelnetham and Market Weston Fens. In 1989 John Muddeman and Toby

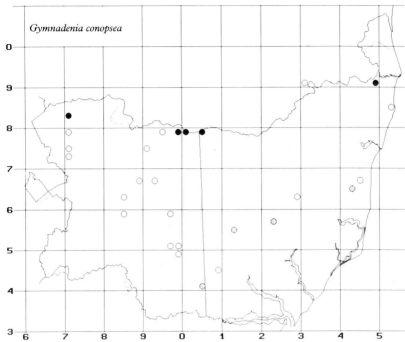

Abrehart discovered five flower spikes in a very rich fen at Barnby. This most interesting new site contains several other rarities. It is the only Suffolk site, for Bog Myrtle (*Myrica gale*) and has recently been scheduled as a SSSI. At Market Weston Fragrant Orchid can be seen in large numbers growing with Marsh Helleborine and several *Dactylorhiza* species. At Redgrave Fen white-flowered plants have occurred for many years, Hind collected a herbarium specimen of '*flore-albo*' there in 1882. There are several 19th century records from marshes around Mildenhall, Tuddenham and Eriswell, but drainage has removed any suitable habitat. There are herbarium specimens collected in the 1840s from Great Barton and Pakenham Fen. Lady Blake collected much material in the Bury area and Pakenham was the source of specimens of a number of rare species. Garnett (1946) reports a site '*near Theberton*' where it grew with Marsh Helleborine. He observed it there from 1942 to 1963 growing in marshes near Holly Tree Farm, with some spikes as tall as 75 cm. Pig farming in the 1960s considerably damaged this site and there have not been any subsequent records.

Drainage is now the major threat to the remaining sites. Even with protection of all sites as SSSIs and as local nature reserves, there is little that can be done to prevent the general lowering of the water table in the Waveney valley area, other than by ceasing to draw water from local bore-holes. All the sites are dependent on calcareous spring water maintaining a particular type of base-rich wet fen. Any changes in the flow or nutrient content of the water soon result in changes in the composition of the fen and the loss of the most sensitive species.

BOG ORCHID *Hammarbya paludosa* (L.) O. Kuntze

The Bog Orchid is one of the most elusive of orchid species; its minute size and yellowish-green flowers make it difficult to find and its flowering is very erratic. The plants are most unusual and have a number of characters which are quite different from most other British orchids. The short aerial stem rises from a pair of pseudobulbs, the upper pseudobulb being covered by two to four small oval leaves. The tips of these fleshy leaves can produce tiny bulbils which drop off to form new plants; this vegetative reproduction can be as important as that from seeds. Flowering occurs in July and August in favourable years. The flower parts are upside down when compared to other orchids; the twisted pedicels show that the flowers are in fact rotated through 360° (in most orchids they are rotated through 180°). It is found in acid bogs where there is *Sphagnum* moss. The plants grow in water-saturated cushions of moss and rely heavily on a mycorrhizal fungus to supply nutrients. This habitat is decreasing both nationally and in Europe as a whole and for this reason Bog Orchid is included in the Red Data Book of threatened species (Perring & Farrell, 1983).

It is well over 100 years since Bog Orchid has been seen in Suffolk. It was always a scarce plant in a county with such a low rainfall and relatively few sites suitable for *Sphagnum* bog. The small area north of Lowestoft, especially the parishes of Belton, Ashby and Herringfleet formed its last

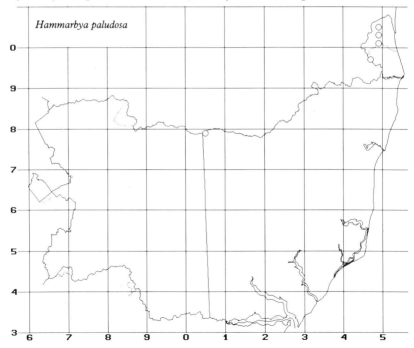

Hammarbya paludosa

stronghold in the early 19th Century, but these bogs were soon enclosed and drained for agriculture. Today there is little sign of the extensive wet commons that once covered much of this area. At that time it was known as *Malaxis paludosa*. The first record for the County was not until 1815 and is confirmed by a specimen in the herbarium at the British Museum collected by J. W. Backhouse at '*West Common, Burgh, Nr. Yarmouth*'. Another specimen collected by Backhouse at Burgh c.1840 is in the herbarium of The Yorkshire Museum. In 1834 the Rev. G. R. Leathes found it '*abundantly*' at Ashby Warren. *Sphagnum* mosses can still be found in this area around Fritton Decoy, though much of the Warren is now planted with conifers. Paget (1834) recorded three species of *Sphagnum* as '*common*' at Belton and other bogs in the area; he also includes a record of Bog Orchid at Belton Common from Dawson Turner. Paget records the enclosure of commons at Hopton and Corton '*for the purpose of cultivation, which is every day lessening the extent of those* [heaths] *that remain*'. Hodskinson's map of Suffolk in 1783 shows how widespread such commons once were in the County and it is quite possible this small orchid occurred at such sites and was overlooked. Commons at Mildenhall and Lakenheath and Fens at Cavenham and Tuddenham were also rich in *Sphagnum* before the extensive drainage schemes of the late 18th and early 19th centuries. Hind (1889) gives an undated record from Redgrave Fen made by T. C. Collins and this site still contains some suitable habitat. Bog Orchid survived at nearby Roydon Fen, on the Norfolk side of the Waveney, until 1937, and still occurs at a very few sites in that County.

MUSK ORCHID *Herminium monorchis* (L.) R. Br.

The Musk Orchid is very small and easily overlooked, but where it grows in quantity, as on Painswick Beacon in Gloucestershire, its inflorescences can form a yellow mass which at a first glance looks like Lady's Bedstraw (*Galium verum*). The whole plant is only 5 to 15 cm high and its leaves, stems and flowers are yellow-green. It can produce tubers on small side shoots as a means of vegetative reproduction, which often leads to the formation of clumps of plants. The flowers are produced in June and July with about twenty to thirty to a spike. They are tubular in shape with toothed petals producing a spiky appearance. The scent is sweet but not musky. It prefers short turf on downs or old pastures and is often found around old quarries. In Britain it is restricted to southern England, nearly always on chalk or oolite. At one time its range extended as far north as Hunstanton in Norfolk, though most East Anglian sites had been lost by 1850.

The Musk Orchid has probably been extinct in Suffolk for over 170 years and was never a common plant in the County. It was found in a chalk-pit at Sicklesmere and at Little Saxham (Henslow & Skepper, 1860), by Sir T. G. Cullum. Both these records were probably taken from Gillingwater (1804). There is also a record for Bury, on the authority of N. J. Winch in The New Botanist's Guide published 1835-7. Many of the open fields in this area

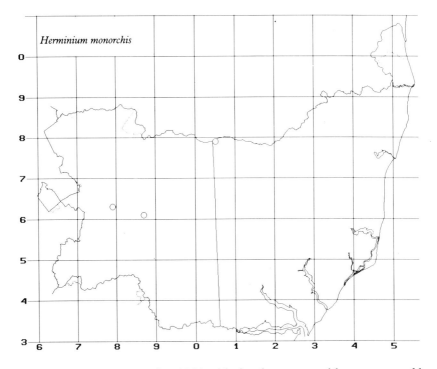

Herminium monorchis

were ploughed up soon after 1800 with the change to arable, encouraged by high corn prices. Sheep grazing, which kept the turf short, moved further north to the poorer soils of the Breck. The past distribution and early decline of the Musk Orchid match that of the Early Spider Orchid and there is reason to believe that it may also have been affected by climatic change. Summerhayes (1968) points out that it is on the edge of its geographical range in Britain.

The record in Simpson (1982) from Redgrave Fen in 1936 by Ronald Burn is most unusual for a species normally found in Britain in short turf on downs or old pastures on chalky soils. I can find no other reference to the species occurring at this site and suspect it is an error.

LIZARD ORCHID *Himantoglossum hircinum* (L.) Spreng.

This most spectacular species is unlikely to be confused with any other orchid in Britain. The leaves are oblong and grey green, forming a bulky rosette which appears in autumn and lasts through the winter. Flower spikes are produced in June and July. These can be very large and often smell strongly of goats. The individual flowers are strangely coloured with a mixture of grey, green and brown; the long (25-45 mm), twisted labellum is brown and white with bright crimson dots. Although about a third of all capsules contain viable seed the species appears to be slow to increase. It is often found as a solitary plant, which only flowers when conditions are suitable.

Lizard Orchid

Throughout the 19th Century the Lizard Orchid was very rare and mainly restricted to the south-east corner of England. The first half of the 20th Century saw a dramatic increase in range, as plants were found as far north as Yorkshire. They appeared 'spontaneously' in many places where the species had not been seen before. About 90% of all records in Britain were of single plants and it is possible that these all arose from windborne seed from France (pers. comm. Mrs. G. Crompton). More recently the species has again declined in range and frequency with only a very few permanent colonies surviving. The best remaining sites are in Kent and Cambridgeshire. The Lizard Orchid is now a protected species under Schedule 8 of the Wildlife and Countryside Act. The rise and fall in the first 70 years of this century correlates well with changes in climate. From 1900 to 1940 the climate was warmer and more equable than in the previous century. During the next thirty years winters became colder and the summers wetter. However, the warmer summers of the past two decades have not resulted in another increase in range.

As in the rest of Britain during the 19th Century the Lizard Orchid was extremely rare in Suffolk with some writers suggesting it had become extinct. The first record for the County, at Marlesford Hall on 13th July 1812, is in an anonymous note in a copy of Rousseau's Letters on the elements of Botany. The only other 19th Century record is from Great Glemham in 1847. The recorder, the Rev. E. N. Bloomfield, an eminent botanist, was quite capable of identifying this most characteristic of species, yet he felt it necessary to send the specimen to Prof. C. C. Babington at Cambridge for 'confirmation'. The specimen is now in the herbarium of the British Museum (Natural History). Bloomfield (1858) later wrote *'Although I have examined the locality almost every year since that time, I have been unable to find a second specimen.'* The original specimen had been completely uprooted with its tubers.

As with other parts of the country the warmer years of the 1920s and 30s produced a number of new records for Suffolk. All of the new sites were in East Suffolk and usually only single plants were found. Several were on gravelly, base-rich soils. At Belstead, Tattingstone (Rowling, 1956*) and Sudbourne it was associated with crag soils with shell fragments providing the calcareous element. Plants were still threatened by collectors and there were at least two herbarium specimens taken in this period. One, now in Oxford University herbarium, was taken at Wangford, near Halesworth in 1917. Here, a single plant was found in an old gravel pit growing on glacial sand and gravel overlying crag. No further plants were found at this site. Another single plant was seen on a roadside verge near Saxmundham in 1921, growing on boulder clay. This site was later destroyed during road mending. At two sites the plants were dug up for 'safe keeping'. At Coddenham (probably Shrubland Park) one was found by a child and picked for the school wildflower competition. The schoolmistress transferred the plant to the school garden and then back to the original site when she retired. At Trimley Marshes a plant

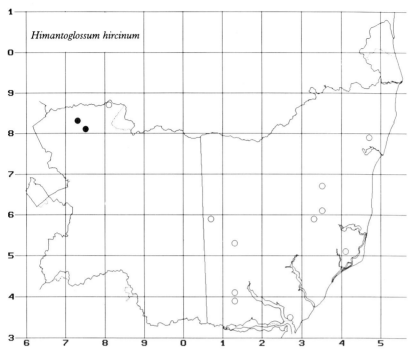

Himantoglossum hircinum

found near the Dooley Fort (this is the Martello Tower mentioned by Summerhayes, 1968) was removed to a garden in Felixstowe. A group of plants was found near a factory at Stowmarket by F. W. Simpson in 1946 (Simpson, 1946); they were growing on a steep bank in loose chalky boulder clay mixed with gravel. Bee and Pyramidal Orchids were also found at this site.

In 1953 the first West Suffolk record was made near Brandon; this plant had to be moved 5 yards as it was right next to a road about to be widened; there is no information on its survival. Nine plants were found on Lakenheath Warren by M. G. Rutterford in 1972 in thin turf over chalk. Two flowered in 1973 and 27 plants were counted in 1974. Sadly the plants suddenly seemed to 'fade away' (pers. comm. M. G. Rutterford) and none were seen there until 1990 when one plant was discovered on the Warren.

The other extant site in the County is the well documented population at Maidscross Hill, Lakenheath; here it grows in calcareous sand (pH 8.0) on disturbed heathland. This is now the most northerly site in Britain for the species. Rutterford (1964, 1975 and 1985) has provided an excellent account of the population since its discovery in 1954 and gives much valuable information about the species. The plant first flowered in 1955. In 1957 and '58 the first young plants appeared; these did not flower until 1965. The original plant continued to flower until 1973, when there was then a gap of ten years when none of the plants produced flowers. On several occasions plants have produced flower buds which later withered away due to prolonged hot dry weather. Plants are in leaf during the winter and are able to withstand frost and snow. However, grazing by rabbits, usually intensified by a cold spell, can cause severe damage. Lesser damage is annually inflicted by slugs and snails. The Maidscross Hill population increased to about 40 plants in 1985 but has since declined rapidly. Only four plants have been found in 1990; these are being damaged by grazing from travellers' horses.

The survival of the Lizard Orchid in the Breck must in part be due to protection of the site as a SSSI. This species is still under threat from thieves who dig up plants (a site in Cambridgeshire has suffered recently from such criminal activity). It is for this reason that details of the locations cannot be released and I would urge anyone who knows the precise locations to keep them a closely guarded secret.

Just over the County boundary in Cambridgeshire the Lizard Orchid can be seen on the Devil's Dyke outside Newmarket. This site contains a wealth of interesting chalk flora. During the summer an orchid warden is employed to protect the plants from vandals.

*N.B. it was not refound at Tattingstone in 1959 – see correction by Heathcote (1986).

FEN ORCHID *Liparis lœselii* (L.) L. C. M. Rich.

The Fen Orchid is a small and inconspicuous species, easily overlooked when growing amongst tall reeds. The three-sided stem arises from a pair of hard pseudobulbs. These are sheathed by a pair of long, oval, shiny yellow-green leaves (in the variety *ovata* the leaves are much shorter and only a little longer than broad). The flowers are carried in a loose spike about 10-15 cm high. They are also yellow-green, with narrow petals. Often they are turned upside down like those of the Bog Orchid. Flowering occurs from mid-June to early July.

In Britain Fen Orchid occurs in wet calcareous (or neutral) fens. The strongest population is in Norfolk, but the variety *ovata* occurs in South Wales on dune slacks and at Braunton Burrows in North Devon. Collectors and more especially drainage of sites have caused its disappearance from many former sites. It is now a protected species under Schedule 8 of the Wildlife and Countryside Act (1981).

Fen Orchid and associated plant communities are found on a specific type of fen flushed with calcareous ground water, often from springs rising through chalk. In such sites it prefers a certain stage of colonisation of pool edges with Blunt-flowered Rush (*Juncus subnodulosus*), sedges and moss. Perring, Sell & Walters (1964) suggest it is reliant on moss communities dominated by *Calliergon (Acrocladium) cuspidatum* and various *Campylium* species growing in very wet fen. These moss communities do not persist permanently and appear to require some sort of disturbance, such as peat-digging. Successful flowering follows cropping of rush and sedge. In following summers the number of spikes decreases as rush and sedge growth returns. Non-flowering plants can survive undetected amongst taller vegetation for many years.

F. W. Simpson

Fen Orchid

The loss of this species from Suffolk is a recent, and sad extinction. It was last recorded in 1974 at Thelnetham Fen. This had always been its best known site in the County. Herbarium specimens were collected there by a number of botanists, including the Rev. J. D. Gray (1883) and J. E. Lousley (1935). Simpson (1982) includes a photograph of a fine colony of plants taken at Thelnetham in June, 1939. Bellamy and Rose (1960) noted '*a number of plants still present on the Suffolk side of the Little Ouse*', but thought it was '*much more abundant at Thelnetham twenty years ago; it occurred in at least one spot as a colony of between 50 and 100 individuals.*' P. J. O. Trist recorded two colonies of eight plants at Thelnetham Old Fen in 1965. It was seen at Hinderclay in 1967 (Simpson, 1982). Many of the small headwater fens are a complex mixture of calcareous wet fen with patches of acidic, raised *Sphagnum* bog. In these habitats it grew with Blunt-flowered Rush (*Juncus subnodulosus*), Black Bog-rush (*Schœnus nigricans*), Great Fen Sedge (*Cladium mariscus*) and Marsh Pennywort (*Hydrocotyle vulgaris*). Other orchids typical of this habitat are the Narrow-leaved Marsh Orchid (*Dactylorhiza traunsteineri*) and the cream-flowered subspecies of the Early Marsh Orchid, (*D. incarnata* ssp. *ochroleuca*). Both these orchids are now on the verge of extinction in Suffolk.

In the 19th century Fen Orchid was also found at Redgrave and Lopham Fens; there is a specimen from Redgrave collected in 1883 in Hind's herbarium at Ipswich Museum. Heathcote (1975), commenting on the falling water table in the area as a result of the East Anglian Water Company's

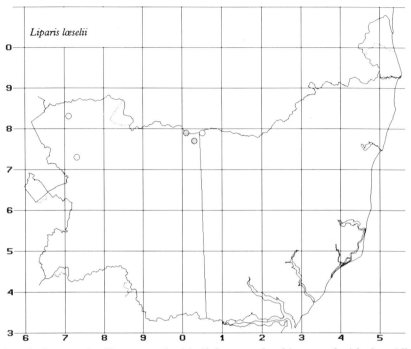

Liparis loeselii

borehole near the Fen, remarked '..*if the water level is not replenished rapidly, it will certainly not encourage the re-establishment of this increasingly rare orchid.*' Sadly, it had probably gone from the County by the time this paper was published.

Fen Orchid also occurred in one or two of the Breck Fens, including Lakenheath and Tuddenham. It was first noted at Tuddenham around 1800 by Sir T. G. Cullum. There is a herbarium specimen at the British Museum collected at Tuddenham by the Rev. E. N. Bloomfield in 1912 (Bloomfield was then 85; he collected the Lizard Orchid at Great Glemham 65 years earlier in 1847!). Its presence in the Breck suggests that these sites were once more calcareous, probably as a result of a higher water table. The major damage to habitats has occurred as a result of land drainage. This affected the Breck Fens from around 1800 onwards with only the more remote areas like Tuddenham surviving into the twentieth century. The water table was lowered by several feet (Haslam, 1965) and without renewed supplies of nutrient-rich ground water these fens first became acidic and later dried out completely. The particular moss communities favoured by this species require interference such as peat digging for their survival. Most peat cutting had stopped by the turn of the century. Heathcote (1975) details similar changes at Redgrave. Drainage in the Waveney/Ouse valley has severely affected all the small tributary fens over the past forty years. The final loss from Thelnetham, whether due to collectors – as Simpson (1982) suggests, or to changes in the habitat, is to be deplored. Perring and Farrell (1983) suggest it is '*one of our most rapidly declining species*' with only eight sites left from thirty known post-1900. They conclude that it '*seems very unlikely that it can survive much longer in East Anglia, where even nature reserves give no protection against the general drainage of the region*'.

The decline of this species has been paralleled not only in the rest of East Anglia, but also on the Continent. Leten (1990) records similar dramatic losses caused by drainage in Belgium, with only five, non-fruiting plants remaining in the country by 1988. He suggests that as the habitat for this species is restored by management on nature reserves (as has happened at Thelnetham Fen), and it seems well adapted to colonising new territory, a re-establishment might occur. Work by Reinecke (1976) has shown it is possible to propagate the Fen Orchid by sowing seeds directly beside the parent plants. He succeeded in raising over 200 plants in 4 years. These flowered after about 7 years, though difficulty was experienced in maintaining optimum growing conditions.

TWAYBLADE *Listera ovata* (L.) R. Br.

The Twayblade is one of the better known orchid species. It is widely distributed and often occurs in large populations. The plants have a pair of large, oval, plantain-like leaves placed a few inches up the stem. In shady sites they will often not flower for many years, but where there is some light the narrow, green flower spikes appear in profusion in April and May. The flowers are small and yellowish-green with a long, two-lobed lip. The plants spread vegetatively as well as by seed and in some woods they can become the dominant ground flora. Twayblade is tolerant of a wide range of soil types from wet to dry and from acid to alkaline. The plant ceases to be dependent on mycorrhizal fungus after about four years' growth which may account for its ability to survive by vegetative reproduction in sites where drainage or soil type have been altered. It is found throughout Britain.

Although a 'tolerant' species, Twayblade still shows a preference for undisturbed sites and is often found in sites where other species of orchid are present. It occurs in virtually all the ancient woodland sites in Suffolk, even in quite small copses and thickets. It is also capable of colonising new habitats such as conifer plantations or chalk pits, the initial seedlings increasing vegetatively to cover quite large areas in a few years. It is tolerant of very heavy shade, a factor which has enabled it to survive in neglected woods where other species have been lost. Single specimens can be found in some of the smaller woods; these are not always ancient sites and they may be new colonisations rather than remnants of larger populations. Other sites include the drier parts of fens (Redgrave) and marshes (Gromford), rough commons and greens (Wortham and Haughley), chalk pits (Barton Mills, where a magnificent population of giant plants flourishes in the Rex Graham Reserve) and old meadows (Monewden). Records from the 19th century suggest it was frequently found in grassland habitats. Many such sites have now been lost to the plough. Overall the species has maintained its widespread distribution in the County but there has been a reduction in the number of sites.

Twayblade

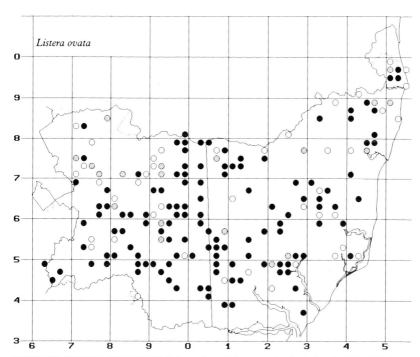

Listera ovata

BIRD'S-NEST ORCHID *Neottia nidus-avis* (L.) L. C. M. Rich.

This is one of the most unusual of Suffolk's orchids. Its brown colour and lack of true leaves make it easy to distinguish. The plant is devoid of chlorophyll and derives its nutrients from rotting humus. The name 'bird's-nest' refers to the ball of roots at the base of the plant; these are associated with a mycorrhizal fungus, which supplies food from the breakdown of the surrounding humus. The flowers are out mainly in June and in a favourable season many spikes may be found in well-established populations, Simpson (1982) records '*sixty spikes in a small wood near Woodbridge*' in 1969. Because the plant is not dependent on sunlight for photosynthesis and requires damp humus for the root ball, it is often found in the darkest corners of dense woods, where shade prevents the soil drying out. Combined with the rather cryptic coloration this makes it difficult to spot. The plant is subterranean except when in flower, although the dead spikes may remain for about a year. It may have been overlooked in some large woods where a complete search is difficult.

In Suffolk, Bird's-nest Orchid is now quite rare with only about a dozen sites remaining. It is almost entirely restricted to ancient woodland, mainly on boulder clay. Peterken (1974) regards it as an 'indicator species' of ancient woods in Lincolnshire and this is also true in Suffolk. Typically these woods have an understorey of Hazel coppice with Ash, Hornbeam or Oak as standards. It seems to prefer mature or over-mature coppice where the light level is low. This sort of habitat is increasingly scarce and mainly found in

82

Bird's-nest Orchid

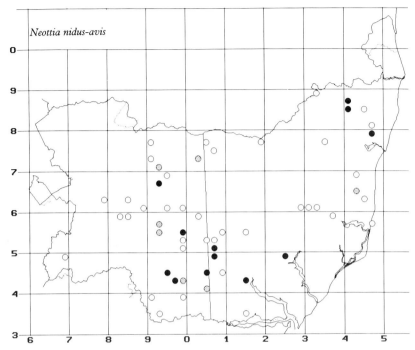

Neottia nidus-avis

undisturbed sites with little or no management. Nearly all the woods where it has been recorded recently have at least one other species of orchid and I suspect it is one of the first species to be lost from woods when they are replanted or suffer excessive disturbance. Some of the best sites are the mid-Suffolk ancient woods around Barking, Offton and Edwardstone. In Groton Wood it occurs in the long-established secondary wood among hazel coppice shaded by standard oaks. It can also be found in woods in the north-east at Redisham and Reydon. Surprisingly, it has not been recorded recently in the Bradfield Woods, although there are old herbarium specimens from Bradfield (Lathbury, 1852) and Cockfield (Hind, 1879). In 1977 it was found amongst Elm scrub in an old railway cutting at Raydon and in 1980 in a small covert in Ipswich (Hyde, Hyde & Simpson, 1981). Many sites were lost during the 19th century when much ancient woodland was grubbed out to make way for more arable farming. Parishes like Hitcham and Nayland lost very large areas of woodland. Some of the woods where the species was recorded in the 19th century are still extant, but have been greatly altered through management and replanting. The further destruction of many woods in the 1940s and 50s for agriculture and the 1960s for coniferisation has left very few sites where the species is safe from disturbance. The fact that there are 19th century records for most sites where the species is still found suggests it can survive for long periods where there is suitable habitat and management. A few of these sites are now managed as reserves, which may give the species some protection.

BEE ORCHID *Ophrys apifera* Huds.

The Bee Orchid must be the most easily recognised and well known of the British orchids. Like other *Ophrys* species it produces a small rosette of grey-green leaves in autumn, which stay green over winter and wither away by midsummer. The flower spikes are produced from early June through to mid-July, each spike carrying between two and seven widely spaced flowers. The large, pointed sepals are pink with green veins. The upper petals are pale brown with rolled margins giving a cylindrical shape like a Bee's antennae; between them rises a greenish beaked column carrying sticky yellow pollen bundles. The rounded labellum is deep velvety brown marked with varying amounts of yellow, often in the shape of an 'H'. With self-pollination seed set is high, with most plants producing tens of thousands of dustlike seeds. A widespread species throughout England, Wales and the central plain of Ireland, it shows a marked preference for calcareous soils, but may also be found on clays, marls and shelly sand dunes.

It is a widespread species in Suffolk, often appearing in large numbers. Erratic flowering makes it a challenge to find and sites which have hundreds of flowers one year may have none the following season. It is mainly concentrated on the chalky boulder clay in a band running from the north-east to the south- west of the County. This pattern is not unlike that of the Pyramidal Orchid with which it often grows. It has a wider range of tolerance than the Pyramidal and can be found on neutral clays and gravels. It is the only

R. C. Dryden

Bee Orchid

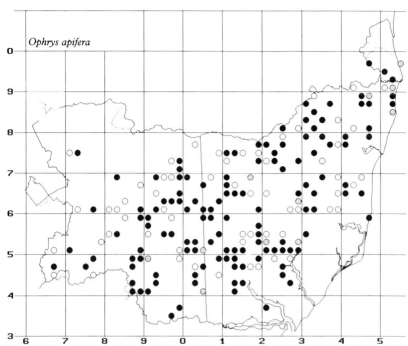

Ophrys apifera

orchid to have been found recently on the Shotley Peninsula. It also occurs at several coastal sites, including cliff tops at Pakefield and Corton and in stabilised dunes by the coast road at Aldeburgh. Occasionally it will occur on crag soils, especially in old pits and other exposed soils. Simpson (1965) found it on crag around Butley and Chillesford. It is capable of rapidly colonising disturbed soils, especially chalky clays. In such sites it is like a ruderal weed (Grime, 1979), dying out quite quickly as more vigorous plants become established. The increased drainage and reduced nutrient content give the orchids (which rely on mycorrhizal fungi for nutrients) a headstart over other plants. Railway cuttings, road banks, spoil heaps, gravel pits and industrial waste ground have all supported populations. At Gisleham it grew in large numbers in an old brick pit until the site was filled with waste; a few plants have survived around the edges of the pit. After the last war it rapidly spread onto the disused airfields and it can still be found at Ellough, Rattlesden and others that have not gone under the plough. It is frequently found on roadside verges, including several protected as nature reserves. At many of these sites, including the well known verge at Great Blakenham, it grows with Pyramidal Orchid and a range of other chalk-loving species. Sites are continually being lost through habitat destruction, especially the filling of old pits and quarries. Unlike most orchids, the high seed set enables it to colonise new sites. When farmland is left fallow for at least five years this species can sometimes appear in large numbers. This occurred in several Suffolk parishes between the wars when much land lay fallow (Simpson, 1982). Morley (1933) gives an example of plants appearing in an old kitchen

M. N. Sanford

M. N. Sanford

Bee Orchid var. *chlorantha*   Wasp Orchid at Cookley

garden at Monk Soham. Several other recorders have found plants in gardens, especially on lawns left unmown in hot weather (Dickinson, 1949). Plants are sometimes dug up and moved to gardens, but as they usually flower and set seed only once before dying (monocarpic – see Ecology), such transplants are rarely successful.

A variety with a light yellow-green labellum and white or pale green sepals has been called var. *chlorantha*. It is really a partial albino lacking anthocyanin pigments. It is perpetuated by self-pollination and is quite frequent at a number of sites in the County. There is a large population on part of the old airfield at Parham and good numbers can be found on the protected roadside verge at Great Blakenham. It occurs on a protected verge at Fressingfield and has also been recorded recently from Dennington, Felsham, Bradfield St. George, Barham and Burgh. There are two specimens in the herbarium at Ipswich Museum, one from Burstall in 1835 and one in Kirby's collection from Huntingfield in 1802.

Several plants of the 'Wasp Orchid', (*O. apifera* var. *trollii*) were found on a roadside verge at Cookley in 1990; the first Suffolk record of var. *trollii* for over forty years. In this distinct variety the tip of the labellum is not curved back and hidden, but continues downwards with a point. It has brown, yellow and green markings but with no clear-cut pattern. F. W. Simpson found var. *trollii* at Whatfield in 1930 (Burn, 1931) and at Monk Soham (Simpson, 1982). Another variation, found by F. W. Simpson at Dallinghoo in 1983, was a 'semi-peloric' mutant in which the two upper petals were like small sepals (Hyde & Simpson, 1984).

FLY ORCHID *Ophrys insectifera* **L.**

The Fly Orchid is one of the more mysterious and elusive species, its dark flowers and thin spikes merge so well with the surrounding vegetation. The dark green basal leaves are long and narrow with a shiny upper surface. They are produced in late autumn, stay green over winter and wither away by early summer. The flower spikes are produced from mid-May through to the end of June. They are slender and quite tall (up to 60 cm) with several widely spaced flowers. The resemblance of the individual flowers to a fly or wasp is very striking. The bright green, broad sepals form an effective foil to the dark petals. The narrow, brown upper petals form the antennae while the rounded labellum forms the body and wings. The labellum is long and narrow with two small, spreading lobes half-way down and a large, notched terminal lobe. It is a rich brown colour and has a velvety texture with a smooth band of iridescent blue across the middle. This shiny band has a wavy outline rather like a fat 'W' and sometimes extends to include the lateral lobes.

The species is quite widespread in south-east Britain with a similar distribution to the Burnt Orchid. As it is not as 'Mediterranean' in its climatic preference, its range extends further north than other *Ophrys* species. It is mainly a plant of woodlands, sometimes in deep shade, but more often in scrub or on the edges of rides. Occasionally it can be found growing in open grassland. It is nearly always associated with calcareous soils and in many sites it is accompanied by several other orchid species.

Fly Orchid is now very rare in Suffolk. There are only two sites in which it has been seen since 1980, one in East and one in West Suffolk. Sadly, for such an attractive (to collectors) and sensitive species the precise location of these sites must remain confidential. Both sites are scheduled as SSSIs and are in woodland on calcareous substrates. The eastern site was first recorded by members of the Ipswich and District Field Club in 1911 and 50 spikes were found there by F. W. Simpson in 1929. Other species at this site include Twayblade, Common Spotted and Bee Orchid. At the western site it has been present for over 100 years. It grows along the edges of a number of open rides on a very chalky soil. Other species found nearby include Pyramidal, Common Spotted, Twayblade, Bee, Early Purple and Greater Butterfly Orchids.

It has been recorded from another five sites since 1950. Sir Cedric Morris knew it in the Hadleigh/Raydon railway cutting in the 1960s. One plant was seen in flower in the cutting in 1970. At Offton it grew in an ancient wood which still retains another six orchid species. Fly Orchids were last recorded there in 1977. Alec Bull recorded it from three sites in the Brett Valley; Whatfield in 1960, Primrose Wood, Hitcham in 1959 and a disused chalk pit at Nedging 1944-58, where it grew with Man and Pyramidal Orchids and Yellow-wort (*Blackstonia perfoliata*) until they were choked out as the pit became overgrown. Simpson (1982) lists a few other parishes where it has been recorded since 1930. I have no more recent information from Hessett, Elmsett, Ringshall, Great Finborough, Barking and Bacton. The only other twentieth century record is from Mendlesham in 1911 (Mayfield, 1911).

I. J. Killeen

Fly Orchid

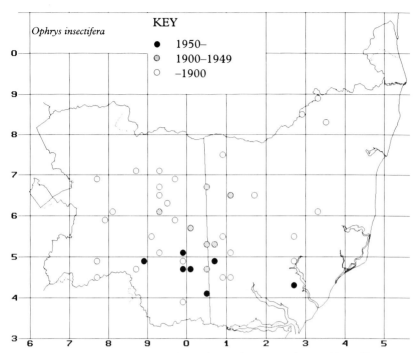

In the 19th century it could be found in many of the mid-Suffolk ancient woods. Specimens collected at Cockfield and Pakenham can be found in a number of Victorian herbaria. Several of these woods are still extant, but without management they have become overgrown with little habitat suitable for Fly Orchid. It also grew in old chalk pits and, in a few places, in open grassland. At All Saints South Elmham it grew in the Rectory field with Autumn Ladies Tresses (Rev. E. A. Holmes in Galpin, 1888). Taylor (1887) recorded it from *'lanes behind Sproughton'*; this is probably the same site as his record from *'Alexander's Farm, Burstall'* given in Hind (1889). The Rev. G. Crabbe recorded it as *'rare in dry pastures near Glemham'* in Hawes (1798).

The sharp decline of this orchid is paralleled by other woodland species such as Greater Butterfly and Bird's-nest Orchids. Although many sites have been lost through the grubbing up of woodland in both the 19th and 20th centuries, there are also many sites in which its disappearance must have been due to lack of management or to more subtle changes.

The Fly Orchid is not very slow-growing, but it does not easily colonise new sites. This may be partly due to low seed production. Pollination is effected by male wasps of the genera *Gorytes* and *Argogorytes* (both these solitary wasp genera have been recorded recently in Suffolk) attempting to copulate with the flowers. Such 'pseudo-copulation' ceases when the female wasps emerge. The limitations of such a finely tuned pollination mechanism may become increased, as solitary wasps are also becoming scarce, due to habitat loss.

EARLY SPIDER ORCHID *Ophrys sphegodes* Mill.

The Early Spider Orchid is a grassland species with a superficial resemblance to the Bee Orchid. It has a basal rosette of grey- green leaves which are shorter and broader than those of the Bee. The flowers are produced in late April and early May; pale green sepals and yellow-green upper petals contrast with the deep brown labellum. The labellum is rounded and velvety like the Bee and marked with a smooth, blue grey 'H'; it has a similar projecting column to the Bee but with two glistening pouches of nectar at each side which look like a spider's eyes. Spikes usually carry two or three flowers and are slightly shorter than the Bee. Colour and shape variations in flowers are quite common, but are not usually given varietal status. It is found in short turf on calcareous soils and shows a preference for older, undisturbed sites. At one time it was widely distributed in England, but most sites north of the Thames had been lost by 1850 and it is now found, mainly in coastal sites, only in Kent, Sussex, Dorset, Hampshire and Gloucestershire. It is listed in the Red Data Book (Perring and Farrell, 1983), which records only thirteen known localities.

This species has not been recorded in Suffolk for nearly 200 years. The sites were all in the chalky area between Bury and Newmarket and correspond with those for Musk and Burnt Orchids. Downland type chalk grassland must once have existed in parishes such as Westley, Great and Little Saxham, Sicklesmere, Ickworth and Chevington. Other species restricted to ancient

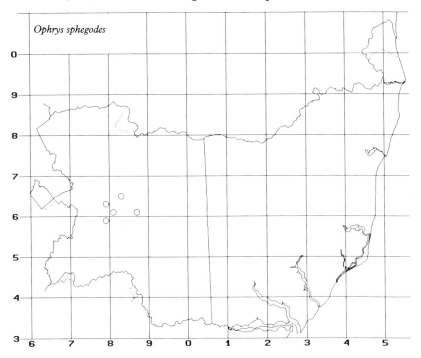

Ophrys sphegodes

chalk grassland were also found in this area. Bastard Toadflax (*Thesium humifusum*), and Pasque Flower (*Pulsatilla vulgaris*) have undergone similar, though more recent, declines. Such grassland often survives around the edges of chalk pits and quarries. The specimen in Kirby's herbarium at Ipswich Museum which provides the last record of the species was probably collected by the Rev. G. R. Leathes; it is labelled '*Ophrys aranifera*' with a note – '*Gathered in a chalk pit, near Bury, April 1793. Very rare indeed*'. The Musk Orchid record at '*a chalk-pit near Sicklesmere*' in Hind (1889) may be from the same site. Another specimen, collected by J. Crowe '*near Bury*' in 1781, is now in the herbarium of Sir J. E. Smith at National Museums & Galleries on Merseyside. There is some doubt about the record in Henslow & Skepper (1860) for a '*chalk-pit at Dallinghœ*'; (they also include records of Fly and Man Orchid from this site), the chalk there is too far down for a pit to be dug and Simpson (1982) suggests it may be an error for Ballingdon, just over the Stour in Essex. Simspon (1990) gives details of an Early Spider Orchid record by John Ray from Ballingdon c.1690 and it was also found there by J. Andrews in 1745. It is possible that some records may have been the result of confusion with partial albinos of the Bee Orchid in which the labellum is brown but the sepals are pale green.

Perring & Farrell (1983) point out that the major decline of this species took place long before the ploughing-up of old chalk and limestone grassland, but in Suffolk much of the open field system west of Bury was brought into cultivation following enclosure acts in the period 1790 to 1840. Earlier sites may well have been destroyed by ploughing in medieval times. Even where arable fields are allowed to return to grass it may be many centuries before they recover the previous diversity of species and some plants, such as Spider Orchid and Pasque Flower may never return.

The present southern distribution suggests that climatic factors may also have been important; it is one of the earliest flowering orchids and may therefore be affected by even minor changes in temperature. Summerhayes (1968) mentions a preference for sites near the sea, suggesting a link with its western distribution on the European mainland.

EARLY PURPLE ORCHID *Orchis mascula* (L.) L.

The Early Purple is one of the best known and most frequently encountered species. The blunt leaves are glossy green and usually marked with large purple blotches of irregular shape. These leaf markings are variable in shape and quantity, and some plants with unspotted leaves can be found in most populations. The tall flower spikes are produced from mid-April through to mid-June and are at their best in May. Some twenty to fifty flowers are carried in a long, lax spike on stems often suffused with purple pigment. The flowers are usually rosy purple in colour with variation in shade from dark purple through to shades of pale pink. White-flowered plants (albinos) are most uncommon. The two upper petals and the upper sepal form a loose hood, while the outer sepals spread back giving a winged appearance to the flower.

92

R. C. Dryden

Early Purple Orchid

The labellum is large with three crenate lobes, the notched central lobe being longer than the reflexed laterals. It is usually paler in the centre and marked with a few small dark dots. A long spur curves upwards from the back of the labellum. The species is widespread and abundant throughout the British Isles. It is commonest in woodlands on calcareous or neutral soils, but can also be found in open chalk grassland and on banks and hedgerows. Plants growing in open turf are shorter and stouter than those in woods.

This species is still widespread in Suffolk; the vast majority of sites are in ancient woodland on boulder clay. The lack of such woodland in the Breck and along the coastal marshes accounts for its absence in these areas. It can occasionally be found in more recent woodland but rarely in large numbers. Early Purple Orchid is an excellent indicator species for old woodland, sometimes surviving after sites have been replanted with conifers, or in hedgerows marking former woodland boundaries. Most ancient sites were managed as coppice with standards. They are rich in tree species and have a characteristic ground flora. Associated species often include Dog's Mercury (*Mercurialis perennis*), Bluebells (*Hyacinthoides non-scripta*), Wood Sanicle (*Sanicula europæa*) and Moschatel (*Adoxa moschatellina*). Its early spring growth has enabled it to survive better in overgrown coppiced woods than summer-flowering woodland species like the Butterfly Orchid. Plants will survive in a non-flowering state in neglected shady woods for many years to reappear, with an abundance of flowers, following clearance or coppicing. Woods have

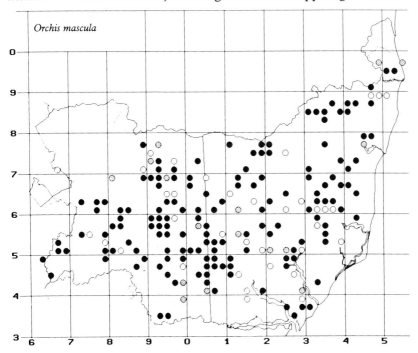

Orchis mascula

been grubbed up all over the County both in the 19th and 20th centuries, but the general pattern of ancient woods has changed little from that of the Middle Ages. In a few woods crag soils provide the required calcareous element.

The major loss of Early Purple Orchids in Suffolk has been from grassland sites. Galpin (1888) and Henslow & Skepper (1860) refer to meadows as typical habitats, but it is now very scarce as a grassland plant. It survives in ancient meadow reserves at Mickfield, Monewden and Cransford, all SSSIs managed by the Suffolk Wildlife Trust. In Martins' Meadow at Monewden it grows in quantity with Green-winged Orchid and, although the flowering periods overlap, no hybrids have been found. It grows with Fritillaries (*Fritillaria meleagris*) in an old meadow at Framsden. I suspect that its survival in grassland was dependent on hay cutting rather than grazing. It is not found in the Green-winged Orchid meadows in the north-east perhaps showing it is less tolerant of trampling and grazing than that species. In a few places Early Purple Orchid occurs on roadside verges, often as a relic of a former woodland edge. Verges with Early Purples have been protected at Wetheringsett, Sweffling, Ilketshall St. Lawrence and Brockley but, being conspicuous, it is unfortunately liable to human depredation.

Several unusual variants have been recorded in the County. These include peloric flowers (in which the petals are all alike) at Needham (Simpson, 1940), Cockfield (1936), Milden and Freckenham (1935). A specimen with spurless flowers named '*O. discalcarata*' collected at Norton by J. Rasor in 1886 is in Hind's herbarium at Ipswich Museum; this is also a peloric form. White-flowered plants have been found at Finborough (1961), Wetheringsett (1984) and Redisham (1988).

MILITARY ORCHID *Orchis militaris* L.

This is one of the rarest and most attractive species to be found in Britain. It is a tall, stout plant with several large, broad, shiny leaves forming a basal rosette. The flower spikes are produced from mid-May to mid-June and are at their best in early June. The spikes are from 20 to 60 cm tall with about thirty faintly scented flowers. The flowers are said to bear a fanciful resemblance to the figure of a soldier. The upper sepals and petals form a pointed hood or helmet, pale lilac on the outside and striped with purple on the inside. The long, pinkish labellum has four lobes, two narrow 'arms' which curve forwards and two broader, squarish lobes which form the 'legs' of the 'soldier'. The 'limbs' are often tinged darker pink, while the 'body' is pale pink or white and usually marked with small dark red spots. Unlike the closely related Monkey Orchid (*O. simia*), the flowers at the bottom of the inflorescence are the first to open.

It appears to be entirely restricted to chalk soils and is usually found where there is some shelter provided by the edges of woods or in scrub. At one time this species was found in several parts of southern England, especially the Chilterns. It became progressively rarer towards the end of the 19th century, partly due to over-collection, and by the 1920s it was considered

I. J. Killeen

Military Orchid

extinct in Britain. In 1947 a small colony was discovered at a new site in Buckinghamshire by J. E. Lousley. In 1954 a colony of about 500 plants was discovered in Suffolk by Mrs. M. Southwell during fieldwork for the BSBI Mapping Scheme. The Suffolk site together with two small colonies in the Chilterns are the only known sites in Britain. This species is protected in Britain under Schedule 8 of the Wildlife and Countryside Act (1981).

The chance discovery of the Military Orchid near Mildenhall must rate as one of the most exciting and surprising finds in the history of Suffolk botany. It is by far the largest population of this species in Britain and a very long way from any of the previous sites. It has been suggested that the colony could have arisen from wind-blown seed at the turn of the century. The area was known to several good botanists in the 19th century and it is most unlikely it would have been overlooked. Since 1955 numbers of plants have varied from about 2600 in 1958 down to about 250 in 1971. Following clearance of Sycamore and Privet in 1972/3 the population stabilised at around 350 plants, with roughly one third flowering in a year. Since the pine margin was cut back in 1985/6 numbers have increased dramatically with over 1100 plants and 279 flowering spikes found in 1990 (see Fig 1.). There is some variation in the colour of the flowers and in the amount of spotting on the labellum. Lang (1980) mentions an unusual plant with long, narrow labellum lobes and found two plants with variegated leaves in 1967. It has been suggested that the Suffolk plants are larger in leaf and inflorescence than those

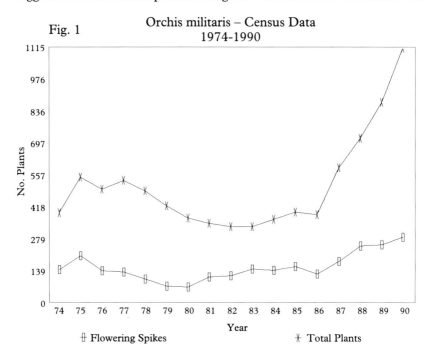

Fig. 1   Orchis militaris – Census Data 1974-1990

No. Plants

Year

⊹ Flowering Spikes   ✳ Total Plants

R. C. Dryden

R. C. Dryden

Military Orchid

Rex Graham Reserve, the best site in
Britain for Military Orchid

in the Chilterns and are more like those of Continental Europe (Sell in Trist,
1979; Farrell, 1985). Research by the S.W.T. Warden in conjunction with
Levington Research Station into environmental differences between the
Suffolk site and a site in the Chilterns in 1989 did not provide evidence of a
genetic difference between the populations.

The site is a long-disused chalk pit in the Butt Plantation in Mildenhall
Woods. The 'Rex Graham Reserve'* is managed by the Suffolk Wildlife Trust
and is scheduled as a SSSI. The Military Orchid grows at the north-eastern
end of the pit on a heap of pure chalk (pH 8.2). Now that encroaching Privet
has been controlled the floor and lower slopes of the pit are covered by damp,
calcareous grassland plants. Other species found in the pit include Twayblade,
Adder's Tongue (*Ophioglossum vulgatum*), Ploughman's Spikenard (*Inula
conyza*), Wall Lettuce (*Mycelis muralis*) and the rare shrub Mezereon (*Daphne
mezereum*).

In 1955, when V. S. Summerhayes and E. Milne-Redhead were shown
the secret site by R. A. H. Graham, the pines in the plantation surrounding
the pit were only about 1.5 m. high, and plenty of sunlight was getting in. The
site was under the protection of the Forestry Commission who had erected
a tall wire fence around the pit, with a padlocked gate to keep unauthorised
people out. It also kept the deer out and allowed Sycamore seedlings to
flourish. When, seventeen years later, in 1972, E. Milne-Redhead, accompanied by P. J. Wanstall and M. Penistan (F. C. Conservator for Eastern
England) visited the pit, it was full of young Sycamore (*Acer pseudoplatanus*)

and Privet (*Ligustrum vulgare*) was starting to dominate the ground flora to the detriment of the Military Orchid. The F. C., with grant aid from the World Wildlife Fund erected a raised and fenced catwalk to prevent damage by trampling visitors and kneeling photographers. The Suffolk Trust for Nature Conservation was urged to recommend the site should be scheduled a SSSI and undertook to remove the Sycamore and start controlling the Privet. The F. C. was asked to remove the nearby Sycamore tree which showered its seeds on the pit, and this was eventually done. More recently the pine trees on the southern side have been felled as they were cutting off all sunlight from the pit from November to February. Opening up the site should make it more attractive to pollinating insects. At present very few seed capsules are produced. The F. C. has created a 'scrape' outside the fence to expose the chalk and so produce a suitable habitat for seedling orchids. Management consists largely of removing seedling birch, cutting back privet and bramble and controlling invasive plants like Coltsfoot (*Tussilago farfara*) and Creeping Buttercup (*Ranunculus repens*). Farrell (1985) gives much useful information about the site and the changes in the population. Public access is restricted to special Open Days organised by the Suffolk Wildlife Trust.

   *Readers may wonder why this site is called the Rex Graham Reserve. Rex was a very active amateur (later professional) botanist and B.S.B.I. referee for Mints, the genus *Mentha*. He became very keen on the conservation of orchids and was shown this site in 1954 by John Raven of Cambridge, a friend of Mrs. Southwell. His tragic death in 1958 at the age of 43 was a great loss to British Botany, and the reserve is a very fitting memorial to him.

GREEN-WINGED ORCHID *Orchis morio* L.

The Green-winged Orchid is a species of particular charm. At suitable sites thousands of dainty spikes can colour a meadow. The small, unspotted, bluish-green leaves are very difficult to see when the plant is not in flower. The short (about 10 cm) flower spikes are produced from late April to early June and are at their best around mid-May. The flowers are large and well spaced giving the spike a fat, squat appearance. Colour can vary from deep blackish-purple through shades of pink and lilac to pure white. The upper sepals and petals form a rounded hood. The outer sepals are marked with a series of green or bronze parallel lines from which the species takes its name. The labellum is large and broad with three lobes; the outer lobes are wide and crenate, often extending beyond the smaller, notched central lobe. The central part of the labellum is pale pink or white and usually marked with a pattern of dark dots. The species is found throughout England and Wales and across the central plain of Ireland. It is most frequent in southern and eastern England in old meadows on neutral and calcareous clay soils. Summerhayes (1968) called it '*one of the commonest of British orchids*', but in recent years it has undergone a dramatic decline as a result of drainage and re-seeding of old pastures. It is still locally abundant but must now be considered a threatened species (Lang, 1980).

R. C. Dryden

Green-winged Orchid, colour forms at Stradbroke Cemetery

In Suffolk there have been serious losses as a result of new intensive farming methods. In the twentieth century many suitable pastures were lost with the change from horse power to tractors. Much habitat had already been destroyed in the 19th century as pastures were ploughed up and converted to arable. The species is now almost entirely restricted to old meadows on central and north-eastern boulder clays. This area corresponds closely with the main dairying region outlined in Young (1813). Dairy pastures suited the damper clay soils well and less land was converted to arable use than in other parts of the County. In this area it is still quite widespread and occurs in wonderful profusion at a number of sites. It is an excellent indicator of old unimproved grassland where it grows in short, often grazed, turf. It is not found on roadside verges and is most typically found in old grazing meadows and pastures. Here it is almost always associated with Cowslips (*Primula veris*) and other characteristic species of undisturbed grassland such as Adder's Tongue (*Ophioglossum vulgatum*). Tiny fragments of the rich flora of these, once widespread, hay meadows have been preserved in Suffolk Wildlife Trust reserves at Monewden, (High House and Martins' Meadows) and at Winks Meadow, Metfield. At Hasketon it is abundant in several meadows with such species as Meadow Buttercup (*Ranunculus acris*), Ladies Smock (*Cardamine pratensis*), Meadow Saxifrage (*Saxifraga granulata*) and Field Woodrush (*Luzula campestris*). In 1985 I came across a peloric mutant at Hasketon in which the the two upper petals were replaced by additional labella (Sanford, 1986). At Monewden it grows in ancient meadows amongst Fritillaries (*Fritillaria meleagris*) and Early Purple Orchids. The most easterly site in Britain is at Gunton, where it grows close to the sea with Adder's Tongue, Twayblade and Common Spotted Orchid. Many sites were lost with the enclosure and ploughing of common land but at Chippenhall Green, perhaps the best known site in the County, it still grows in great profusion. It can also be found on Greens at Southolt and Haughley and on Commons at Mellis, Stuston and Ilketshall St. Andrew. Coyte (1796) includes an interesting early record from a survey of grassland at Tannington Green in 1795. It can occasionally be found in churchyards, and at Stradbroke it is abundant in an old cemetery. In the 1930s it was found on crag soils at Martlesham and in 1926 with Early Purple Orchid and hybrids at Waldringfield (Simpson, 1982). E. Milne-Redhead collected a specimen, now at Kew, from Butley Ferry in 1933.

The species had been lost from most of West Suffolk before the turn of the century. The drier clays, sands and chalks in this part of the County are unlikely to have held large populations. Most sites were in small meadows along the river valleys. It survived in an old meadow at Hitcham until the 1960s and a few plants were seen by C. J. Lowe at Groton in 1975. Simpson (1948) recorded it at East Bergholt in a meadow with Wild Daffodil. In the 1940s it could still be found at Sudbury, Little Cornard, Hawstead, Little Saxham, Barnham and Barton Mills. M. G. Rutterford knew it from pastures between Undley Delph and the old Lakenheath Lode (it was recorded from the same area by Sir C. J. F. Bunbury in the 1850s). This area was ploughed about 1943. The sole surviving site in this part of the County is a fascinating

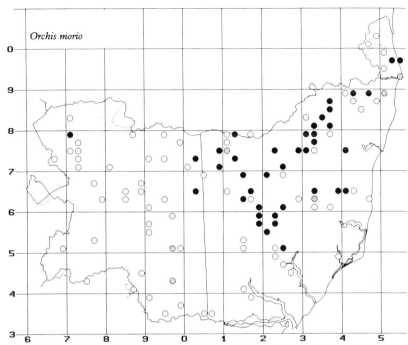

meadow at Wilde Street, Mildenhall. At this SSSI it is frequent in an old unploughed pasture on peaty sand; its undulating surface is crossed by ditches to drain water from the chalk ridge. Here it is not only associated with the usual Adder's Tongue and Cowslips but also with Bugle (*Ajuga reptans*), Stemless Thistle (*Cirsium acaule*) and Large Wild Thyme (*Thymus pulegioides*) (Trist, 1979).

There is little to suggest that the rapid decline of this species has been arrested. Although a few large populations are protected in SSSIs, the majority of sites are private meadows. Small populations are easily destroyed by drainage, reseeding and application of fertilisers and herbicides. Often these operations have been carried out with the incentive of government grant aid. Landowners should be informed of the presence of these rare plants and of the detrimental effect of much 'improvement' on grazing meadows. Such 'improvements' can be far more damaging than leaving sites ungrazed to be taken over by scrub. An example from an Essex Trust Reserve five miles from the Suffolk border has shown that the Green-winged Orchid can survive for 30 years or more in a meadow after grazing has ceased and hawthorn scrub is allowed to develop. At this site, known as Iron Latch Meadow, hawthorn scrub had grown into a closed canopy wood, with practically bare ground beneath; a splendid site for wintering thrushes. The warden, having heard from local people that years ago the grazed meadow was purple with orchids, got permission to clear a small area to let in the sunlight. To everyone's delight Green-winged Orchid plants came up and flowered. Now, with further clearing, a species-rich meadow is developing. The individual orchid plants had survived, almost leafless, in the dense shade for about 30 years!

BURNT ORCHID *Orchis ustulata* L.

The Burnt Orchid is a very small species with attractive flower spikes topped by dark red-brown buds. The stems are about 7 cm tall and carry a number of sheathing leaves; they arise from a rosette of short broad leaves. The sweet-scented flowers are borne in dense spikes which appear from early May to mid-June. The dark upper petals and sepals form a hood which contrasts with the white labellum. The labellum is marked with dark crimson dots and is three-lobed with a long middle lobe which is notched at the tip. Burnt Orchid can take several years to flower from seed. For this reason it is usually found only in undisturbed pastures, favouring old chalk downland with short turf, particularly sheltered south-facing slopes. It cannot survive long when grass grows up after grazing stops. It is mainly found in southern and south-eastern England and although many sites have been lost as pastures are disturbed it can still be seen in some numbers in a few southern counties.

Burnt Orchid has been extinct in Suffolk for many years. The two 20th century records given in Simpson (1982) both seem unlikely. The species was not found in the 19th century at either of these sites. Sir Cedric Morris listed several orchid species from the Hadleigh railway cutting in a letter to Miss Willis (botanical recorder for the Suffolk Naturalists' Society) in 1961. Burnt Orchid is not mentioned and I can only assume that a reference to 'Sweet-scented' orchid was taken to be this species. The Shelland record is from June, 1925 (not 1921 as in Simpson, 1982). Frank Woolnough, in 'Nature Notes' No. 273 in the East Anglian Daily Times, replied to a correspondent – '*Shelland. – The greenish specimen of orchis you send is the dwarf orchis (O. ustulata)...*'. Woolnough was not an expert botanist and the description 'greenish' does not fit the Burnt Orchid; I think this must have been an error. A specimen in the herbarium at Bolton Museum collected by G. S. Mason at Bungay, probably before 1900, may, as Simpson (1990) suggests, have been from the Bath Hills on the Norfolk side of the Waveney. The only undisputed 20th Century record is from Risby [almost certainly the Black Ditches] in 1939 where it was seen by J. E. Lousley and E. C. Wallace.* (I am very grateful to Mrs. E. M. Hyde for showing me this record in Lousley's copy of Hind's Flora lent to her.) There are numerous 19th century records from this site. There are specimens collected at Risby Heath by W. Jordan in Hind's herbarium at Ipswich Museum (1877) and at the British Museum (1880). It had been known at this site for over a century since the first County record there by Sir John Cullum in June 1773. Hind (1889) also gives records for Dalham (the Rev. F. Tearle) and Cavenham – '*In and near the large plantation of Scotch Firs before you come to Cavenham, chalky and dry*' – Sir J. Cullum. [This may also be the Black Ditches which are on the Cavenham parish boundary.] A record from Newmarket Heath in Hind is probably from the Devil's Dyke (Henslow & Skepper, 1860) and made by D. E. Davy around 1828. This site is just over the border in Cambridgeshire. Both Risby Black Ditches and the Devil's Dyke are ancient earthworks. Earthworks in the

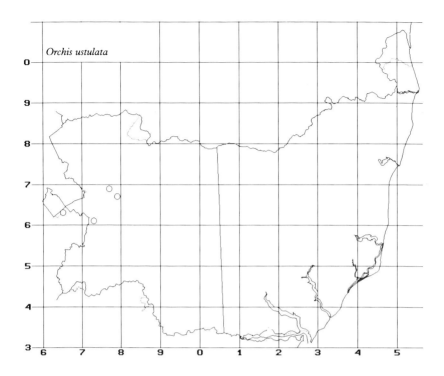

Breck bring the pure chalk to the surface creating a contrast with the surrounding sandy soils. Such areas of unimproved chalk grassland are now very rare in East Anglia. They retain some of the species-rich sward with species such as Squinancy Wort (*Asperula cynanchica*) and Bastard Toadflax (*Thesium humifusum*) more typical of the Downs of southern England. Although both sites are now protected as SSSIs they are still suffering greatly from lack of grazing and scrub encroachment.

The few records suggest Burnt Orchid was never common in Suffolk, and apart from its survival at Risby it had gone from much of the County before 1840. The ploughing of open fields like 'Risby Downs' and 'Cavenham Field' shown on the O. S. Maps of the 1830s resulted in the rapid loss of this species. Foley (1990a) suggests that the most frequent cause of decline in southern England has been agricultural improvement. Simspon (1990) includes details of a Burnt Orchid specimen in Dale's herbarium at the British Museum collected by J. Andrews at Sudbury pre-1757; this may have been on the Essex side of the Stour. Andrews also found Early Spider Orchid at Ballingdon in 1745; these two species had a very similar distribution.

*It was <u>not</u> seen at Risby by M. G. Rutterford as reported in Simpson (1990).

BUTTERFLY ORCHIDS *Platanthera* ssp.

GREATER BUTTERFLY ORCHID *P. chlorantha* (Cust.) Rchb.
LESSER BUTTERFLY ORCHID *P. bifolia* (L.) L.C.M. Rich.

The two species of Butterfly Orchid, Greater and Lesser, are very similar in appearance and cannot be distinguished on size alone. Both species are quite tall (up to 60 cm) with a pair of long, shiny, oval leaves at the base of the stem. Several small stem leaves merge with the pointed floral bracts. They are both in flower from the end of May to the beginning of July. The flowers are well spaced in a lax spike; they are greenish-white with a powerful sweet fragrance. The spike is larger and broader in *P. chlorantha* and often has more flowers than *P. bifolia*. Both species have long white outer sepals spreading horizontally and a narrow, greenish, strap-shaped labellum. In *P. chlorantha* the long spur tends to curve downwards whilst in *P. bifolia* it is more or less straight and projects horizontally across the spike. The important distinguishing character between the species is the position of the two pollen masses (pollinia). In *P. chlorantha* they are placed on either side of the spur with the tops sloping together to form an inverted 'V' and the entrance to the spur is clearly visible., In *P. bifolia* they are placed close together and lie parallel so that the throat of the flower is obscured. These features are constant in both species and the difference is easily observed.

The species differ in their habitat preference. As Simpson (1982) points out, the names 'Wood Butterfly Orchis' for the Greater, and 'Field Butterfly Orchis' for the Lesser, used by Hind are quite appropriate. *P. chlorantha* is mainly found in woodlands on calcareous soils; it is often found along the edges of open rides in company with other orchid species. It also occurs in rough pastures and undisturbed grassland, usually on base-rich soils. It is found mainly in southern England and western Scotland with lesser populations in central Britain. *P. bifolia* is also occasionally found in woods, but is mainly a plant of damp heathy pastures, usually with an acid or neutral substrate. It is quite common in northern and western Britain with small populations scattered throughout the country. It has become much less frequent in southern Britain with the destruction of many lowland heaths. This species can still be found at several sites in Norfolk on acid soils of bogs and wet heaths.

These two orchids were formerly regarded as forms of the one species, *Habenaria bifolia*. Nevertheless, these forms and their habitat preferences were recognised as distinct in several early floras. *P. chlorantha* was sometimes denoted as form 'α' and *P. bifolia* as form 'ß'. Although Greater Butterfly Orchid is now the only species found in Suffolk it cannot be assumed that this was always the case. Many older records could be either species. Lesser Butterfly Orchid can be found alongside the Greater in some southern beechwoods. Dismissal of old *P. bifolia* records simply on the grounds of habitat is not justified. I think the Lesser Butterfly Orchid did occur locally on damp Suffolk heaths but died out between 1860 and 1900 as the few remaining sites were ploughed up. The records in Galpin (1888) for Weybread

R. C. Dryden

Greater Butterfly Orchid

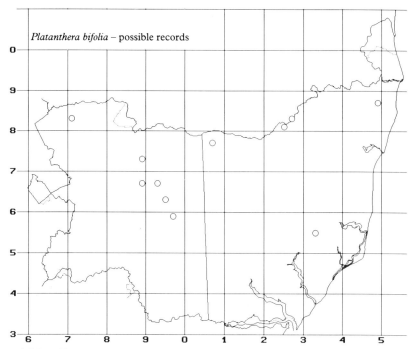

Platanthera bifolia – possible records

and Mendham are quite convincing. Other possible sites given in Hind (1889) include Troston, Rattlesden, Henstead (W. M. Crowfoot) and near Barton Mere (Sir T. G. Cullum who recorded 'major' and 'minor' in Gillingwater (1804)). Simpson's (1988) additions to Hind's list from Tostock (W. H. Tuck) and Campsey Ash (R. Sheppard) are likewise not unlikely. I have seen two herbarium specimens from Suffolk which may well be this species. One, in the British Museum, was collected by J. W. Tuck at Wortham in 1837. He also collected specimens of Twayblade, Southern Marsh and, more significantly, Heath Spotted Orchid at Wortham on the same day. Suitable habitat still exists for this species at Wortham Ling. The other specimen, in Cambridge University herbarium, was collected at Pakenham in 1836. I have heard reports that it may have occurred at Lakenheath Poors Fen before parts of the site were ploughed in the 1960s.

The Greater Butterfly still survives in a number of ancient woods in the County. The best sites are in the mid-Suffolk woods on chalky boulder clay and in one or two ancient woods in the north-east. Like the Fly Orchid, it keeps good company; the majority of sites in Suffolk have at least two other orchid species. At Middle Wood, Offton it grows in profusion with five other species. At Westleton I have seen it growing in old marl pits in an interesting association with Common Cow-wheat (*Melampyrum pratense*). Plants can remain unseen in a vegetative state for many years, only to reappear following coppicing. This species has undergone a serious decline over the past 100

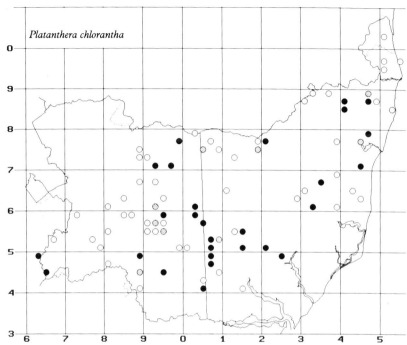

years. Nineteenth century records show that it was found in many more woodland sites throughout mid-Suffolk and in the north-east. The losses have been the result of woods being grubbed out and of lack of management in many of the remaining woods. Cessation of coppicing and the replanting of several woods with conifers has also done much damage. Sites are still being lost for the same reasons. As with the Broad-leaved Helleborine, protection of sites as SSSIs and reserves has not always prevented loss.

AUTUMN LADY'S TRESSES *Spiranthes spiralis* (L.) Chevall.

This charming little orchid is often overlooked because of its small stature and pale flowers. Rosettes of four or five, short, broad, blue-green leaves are formed in September; they persist over winter and die back the following summer before the flower spike emerges. Even in short turf the rosettes can be difficult to spot and plants may often spend a year or more underground with no aerial parts showing. The short flower spikes (5 to 15 cm) appear quite late in the season (mid-August to the end of September); they carry up to twenty small flowers in a single, tight spiral. The flowers are pale greenish-white with a frilled labellum and no spur. During the day they have a faint, but sweet scent. Flowering tends to be very erratic with thousands of spikes appearing in one year and none in another. Growth from seeds can be very slow, but the plants also reproduce vegetatively to produce small, crowded

R. G. Dryden

Autumn Lady's Tresses

populations. Wells (1981) has shown that individual plants can be very long-lived. Autumn Lady's Tresses is a plant of open, chalky pastures and short calcareous grassland and can be found in large numbers on domestic lawns and also on clifftop turf by the sea. It is mainly restricted to southern Britain and Ireland with major populations in the south-east.

Today, the single Suffolk site is at Theberton (Hyde & Simpson, 1984). Here it grows in a private garden on a tennis court and was first noticed in 1983 when reduced mowing in the hot summer allowed hundreds of plants to flower. There are no other records over the last thirty years and the species has been very rare in the County since the turn of the century. There are only eight other post-1900 records. In the early 19th century it appears to have been quite widespread on the chalk pastures around Dalham and Gazeley and in damp meadows around Groton, Cockfield and Shelland. It was also common in the Bungay area on chalky boulder clay, and was present in the Rectory field at All Saints South Elmham with Fly Orchid in the 1880s. In a few places in the Sandlings it occurred on crag outcrops. Zincke (1893) noticed several plants in a damp meadow near crag pits at Stalls Valley, Wherstead around 1847. At Nayland the Rev. J. D. Gray found it, also in a damp meadow, near the Stour. In the Breck it was less frequent; the only record is from a roadside at Holywell Row, near Mildenhall around 1850.

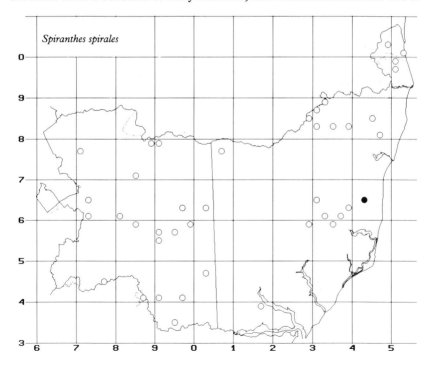

Spiranthes spirales

Several records refer to rectory lawns; turf for these lawns was usually taken from local pastures and the short mowing regime would have suited this species. It still occurred on the Rectory lawn at Whatfield in the 1930s. The small basal leaves are short enough, like those of the Daisy (*Bellis perennis*), to escape the blades of the lawnmower, which removes the inflorescences before they are noticeable. It may well survive unnoticed in many Suffolk lawns. Two other records from the 1930s were in Lothingland (Anon, 1931) at Hopton, in a marshy but not chalky meadow (there is also a herbarium specimen at Norwich Castle Museum collected from Hopton in 1928), and at Belton Heath where it was found with the rare Moonwort (*Botrychium lunaria*). Hind (1889) did not record the species from this area. This heathland record is interesting; it was found at Wortham Ling in the 19th century and in *'Rich fen pasture'* at Ingham Fen by M. Pallis in 1915. At Newton Green it survived on the Golf Course, a remnant of the former heath. A herbarium specimen, collected on the Golf Course by B. S. Rose in 1952, is in the British Museum. The other twentieth century records are Benhall – 1946, Great Glemham – 1956 and Ilketshall St. Lawrence – 1957. Although Summerhayes (1968) suggests it is capable of colonising newly available habitats such as ploughed land which has reverted to grass, this does not appear to have happened in Suffolk, perhaps because sites were too thinly scattered for seed to reach potential new habitats.

Many sites for this species must have been destroyed as grazing pastures were ploughed up in the early 19th century. Much of the open downland around Newmarket and to the west of Bury was enclosed and converted to arable during this period. Short turf lasted longer in the grazing marshes and meadows around the Waveney Valley and on the sheep walks of the Sandlings.

Many of the remaining sites in Britain are now mown rather than grazed and flowering only occurs in dry years when mowing stops in mid-summer. Research has shown that this species can only survive for a limited period after mowing or grazing has stopped and it becomes swamped by taller grasses and herbs. Its survival at such sites is dependent on the maintenance of short turf and in private gardens provision should be made for correct management to be continued following changes of ownership.

HYBRIDS

Hybridisation has greatly complicated the identification of British orchids. Hybrids can show a complete range of intermediate forms between the parents and in some situations 'hybrid swarms' can be found in which virtually no pure parent plants can be found. Crosses can occur at various taxonomic levels, between different varieties and subspecies of a species (intraspecific), between different species of the same genus (interspecific) and between species belonging to different genera (intergeneric). The Orchidaceae is one of the few families in which crosses between species in different genera are at all common and in which they can produce fertile offspring. Stace (1975) gives details of all hybrids known to have occurred in Britain.

In some cases hybrid plants are quite obvious, particularly when occurring as single plants with hybrid vigour. Many crosses, however, can be much harder to detect and in difficult cases it is necessary to examine pollen stained with carmine or orcein. This can be a guide as to which plants are hybrids, but will not identify the putative parents. Many hybrids are not entirely sterile and may back-cross with either parent to produce a range of forms and considerably complicate the issue.

Relatively few hybrids were recorded during the survey and in many cases they are overlooked or misidentified as one or more species. Some hybrid swarms involving *Dactylorhiza* species have resulted in records of four or more separate species being made for the same site. The distribution of hybrids usually reflects the pattern of one or both of the parent species. As hybrids are often more vigorous in growth they may persist in conditions which one or both parent species can no longer tolerate. Such distributions may provide information about the past range of species. In some cases pure strains of the parents may be 'hybridised out' over a long period of time. Maps have only been produced where there are enough records to show a pattern.

Broad-leaved × Violet Helleborine
Epipactis helleborine × E. purpurata
E. × schulzei P. Fourn.

This has been recorded in several of the woods where the Violet Helleborine grows, but can also occur in woods where there is only Broad-leaved Helleborine, as at Bradfield Woods. Simpson (1982) records the hybrid from Lucy Wood, Elmsett in 1930 (a site grubbed out in the 1960s). As both parent species are quite variable, particularly in flower colour, identification of hybrids requires expert confirmation. Hybrids should have leaves longer than the Violet Helleborine but retaining their lanceolate shape and violet suffusion, and flowers with the dull purple coloration of the Broad-leaved Helleborine rather than the clear pale green and mauve of the Violet; such plants are apparently fertile.

Dactylorhiza ssp. × *Gymnadenia conopsea*
× *Dactylogymnadenia*

Hybrids between Fragrant Orchids and all species of dactylorchid can occur naturally. In most Suffolk sites for Fragrant Orchid there are at least two *Dactylorhiza* species present and it is very likely that hybrids will occur as flowering periods have a considerable overlap. Plants looking like Fragrant Orchid but with leaf spots or labellum markings and plants with dactylorchid appearance but strongly scented flowers, may well be hybrids, but in many cases × *Dactylogymnadenia* crosses are very difficult to distinguish from the parents. I have not found any records from Suffolk sites, but I suspect such crosses may well have occurred in the past when Fragrant Orchid was more widespread.

Early Purple × Green-winged Orchid
Orchis mascula × *O. morio*
O. × *morioides* Brand.

This hybrid is surprisingly rare considering the similar flowering seasons of the parents. The two species are found growing together in a few old meadows and many Green-winged Orchid sites have woods with Early Purple Orchid nearby. Hybrid plants have flowers like those of Early Purple Orchid with the green-veined sepals of the Green-winged Orchid; leaves may be spotted or unspotted depending on the Early Purple Orchid parent. Summerhayes (1968) suggests that the similarity between the two species has led to the hybrid being frequently overlooked. The only record from Suffolk is that of Simpson (1982); he found it in a damp pasture at Waldringfield in 1926, growing with both parents on alluvium mixed with Red Crag and broken shells.

Dactylorhiza

Virtually all the species in this genus are capable of hybridising with one another to produce a baffling range of variation. Most of these hybrids are sterile and quite rare. Crosses between the Southern Marsh Orchid and either of the two spotted orchids are not unusual and may be found in large numbers at some sites. Hybrids can involve more than two species, making accurate identification almost impossible.

Common Spotted × Heath Spotted Orchid
D. fuchsii × *D. maculata*
D. × *transiens* (Druce) Soó

This hybrid occurs where acid and alkali soils are found in close proximity. Plants are usually found singly and may exhibit considerable hybrid vigour.

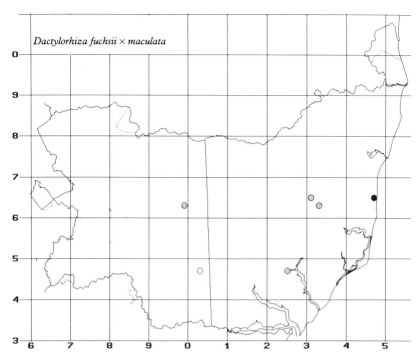

Dactylorhiza fuchsii × maculata

They show a mixture of characters from both parents. The leaves are narrower than those of the Common Spotted with the lowest leaves less rounded at the tips. The flower spikes are long and cylindrical as in the Common Spotted, but with the individual flowers more heavily marked with broader, more crenate labellum lobes. In Suffolk, there have been four confirmed records and it is likely it has been overlooked at other sites. Willis (1963) gives an account of a complex swarm at Martlesham where a swamp probably overlying calcareous crag deposits brought together three dactylorchid species. Specimens sent to Kew were identified by P. F. Hunt as this hybrid. At Cransford Meadow (a SWT reserve) it was recorded by F. W. Simpson in the 1970s with both parents. Simpson (1982) also recorded it at Whatfield in 1937. Ronald Burn recorded many variants of both Common Spotted and Heath Spotted Orchids from this parish in the early 1930s and it is likely some of his records may have been this hybrid. Milne-Redhead (1988) gives details of a single specimen found at Elmswell in 1979 with no other spotted orchids present. This site was being bulldozed and the plant was taken to Kew where it has grown to a great size, producing as many as twenty flower spikes in a season. Simpson (1982) also found it at Sizewell in 1967 and it was still to be found when the site was surveyed in 1984 (confirmed from a photo, Dr. I. A. Denholm, 1989) prior to the building of the Power Station. Plants from this site were transferred to the University of East Anglia during construction and it is hoped they can be returned to the area when disturbance has ceased.

Common Spotted × Early Marsh Orchid
D. fuchsii × D. incarnata
D. × kernerorum (Soó) Soó

As with *D. × transiens* this hybrid is sterile and is usually found singly in mixed populations of both parents. Plants are taller than the Early Marsh Orchid with pale green, hooded leaves sometimes with pale spots. Flowers usually show the flesh-pink base colour of the Early Marsh with a flat, three-lobed labellum and a broad conical spur shorter than that of the Common Spotted Orchid. Sites with both species growing together are mainly found in base-rich fens in the Waveney valley. The sole record of this hybrid from Suffolk is that of Simpson (1982); he found it at Redgrave Fen, in 1937.

Common Spotted × Southern Marsh Orchid
D. fuchsii × D. prætermissa
D. × grandis (Druce) P. F. Hunt

This is a widespread hybrid and may be found with the parents in marshes, wet meadows and fens. Plants are usually tall with narrower leaves than the Southern Marsh Orchid, often with faint, transversely-elongated, solid spots. The flower spikes are conical with densely packed flowers and long narrow bracts. Although the pollen is sterile, some seed is set and swarms of intermediates can be found showing a complete range between the parents.

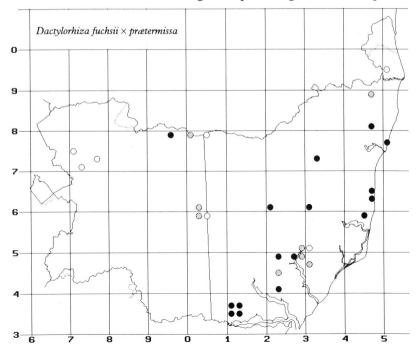

There has been much confusion between this hybrid and the spotted-leaved form of the Southern Marsh known as the Leopard Marsh Orchid, *D. prætermissa* var. *pardalina* (Sanford, 1988). This variety usually has annular leaf markings and is more fertile than the hybrid. It can be found in mixed populations with the type species and many intermediate forms. Whether these are intraspecific crosses or simple phenotypic variation is not clear. Confusion with *D.* × *grandis*, which Simspon (1982) and others have given as a synonym of '*Orchis pardalina*' makes it very difficult to assess past records for this hybrid. Most Suffolk records have been from sites which contain the Southern Marsh, but very few also have the Common Spotted Orchid. Mitchell (1955) gives a good description of this hybrid from the Stowmarket area. Despite the lack of confirmed records, due to problems with identification I am sure it is still quite frequent in Suffolk. Large populations can be found in some of the marshes around Minsmere and Leiston, and at Bentley. F. W. Simpson found six '*varied specimens*' on the edge of a small wet wood at Great Bealings in 1982 (Hyde, Hyde & Simpson, 1983). An early record from marshes at Mildenhall was made by W. C. Barton in 1916. He must have decimated many plants to produce the large number of duplicate herbarium sheets which can still be seen in herbaria at London, Cambridge, Norwich and Ipswich.

Heath Spotted × Southern Marsh Orchid
D. maculata × *D. prætermissa*
D. × *hallii* (Druce) Soó

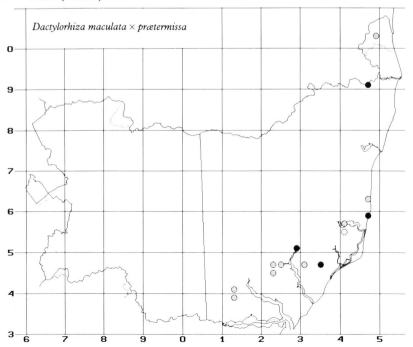

Dactylorhiza maculata × prætermissa

This hybrid is similar in appearance to *D. × grandis* but perhaps even more difficult to distinguish. The leaves are longer and narrower with variable spotting. The labellum has three shallow lobes with the lateral lobes rounded and somewhat crenate. It is marked all over with a pattern of lines and dots. Simpson (1982) has a fine illustration of the flower spikes on p. 520. It appears to be more fertile than other hybrids in this group leading to the development of complex swarms from back-crosses with the parent species. In Suffolk, recent confirmed records have been from Aldeburgh, Barnby, Melton and Bentley. This hybrid was also present at the Sizewell 'B' site and plants were moved to UEA for safe-keeping.

Early Marsh × Southern Marsh Orchid
D. incarnata × D. prætermissa
D. × wintoni (A. Camus) P. F. Hunt

Plants of this hybrid closely resemble the Southern Marsh Orchid and it is very likely to be overlooked. The leaves are yellowish-green and more or less hooded. The flower spikes are narrow with long, often incurved bracts. Flower colour will vary with the Early Marsh Orchid parent. They are smaller than those of the Southern Marsh and have a more distinctly three-lobed labellum. The lateral lobes are often reflexed. It is a sterile hybrid and usually

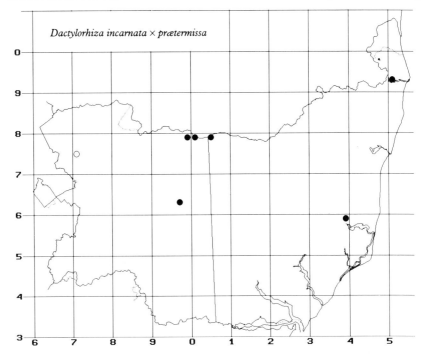

Dactylorhiza incarnata × prætermissa

occurs as single plants in typical Early Marsh Orchid habitats. It has been recorded from several of the Waveney valley fens including Redgrave, Market Weston, Thelnetham and Butchers Marsh, Oulton. A herbarium specimen collected at Thelnetham in 1938 is in the British Museum (Natural History); the hybrid was still there in 1983. It was found in a marshy pasture at Drinkstone in 1981 by E. Milne-Redhead (Hyde, Hyde & Simpson, 1982) and at Gromford during a BSBI meeting in 1988.

Southern Marsh × Narrow-leaved Marsh Orchid
D. prætermissa × *D. traunsteineri*

This hybrid is fully fertile and appears to back-cross to form a complete range of intermediates between the parents. With such similar species producing fertile offspring it is not possible to give clear characters that will distinguish hybrids. David Lang and Dr. I. A. Denholm have both reported the presence of this hybrid at Market Weston Fen. David Lang suggests that the hybrid is more robust and tolerant of drier conditions. This may be leading to its taking over from the Narrow-leaved Marsh Orchid at sites that are drying out. Where one or two hybrids were found in the 1960s there are now more than a hundred and it is becoming difficult to find any pure Narrow-leaved Marsh Orchid. This problem has also been noticed on the Continent (Davies & Huxley, 1988) Dr. Denholm regards both the Southern Marsh Orchid and the Narrow-leaved Marsh Orchid as subspecies of the widespread European species *D. majalis* (Bateman & Denholm, 1983). He refers to a '*morphological continuum*' between the subspecies and suggests this may be due to '*secondary introgression*' or the subspecific boundaries being less clear cut than elsewhere.

USEFUL ADDRESSES

Natural History and Botanical Societies

SUFFOLK NATURALISTS' SOCIETY – c/o The Museum, High Street, Ipswich IP1 3QH

BOTANICAL SOCIETY OF THE BRITISH ISLES – c/o The Department of Botany, The Natural History Museum, Cromwell Road, London SW7 5BD

Conservation Organisations

SUFFOLK WILDLIFE TRUST – Park Cottage, Saxmundham IP17 1DQ
Many Suffolk Wildlife Trust reserves are referred to in the text of this book. For details of access to these sites please read the Reserves Handbook or contact the Trust (see address above).

CONSERVATION ASSOCIATION OF BOTANICAL SOCIETIES – 323 Norwood Road, London SE24 9AQ

PLANTLIFE – c/o The Conservation Foundation, 1 Kensington Gore, London SW7 2AR

IUCN SPECIES SURVIVAL COMMISSION, ORCHID GROUP – c/o Joyce Stewart, Sainsbury Orchid Fellow, Royal Botanic Gardens, Kew, Richmond, Surrey TW9 3AB

Other

SUFFOLK BIOLOGICAL RECORDS CENTRE – c/o The Museum, High Street, Ipswich IP1 3QH

BIOLOGICAL RECORDS CENTRE – NERC Institute of Terrestrial Ecology, Monks Wood Experimental Station, Abbots Ripton, Huntingdon, Cambs. PE17 2LS

USEFUL PUBLICATIONS

Angel, H., 1977, *British Wild Orchids*. Jarrold, Norwich.

Blackmore, S., 1985, *Bee Orchids*. Shire Natural History, Aylesbury.

Davies, J. & P. & Huxley, A., 1988, *Wild Orchids of Britain and Europe*. Hogarth Press, London.

Lang, D., 1980, *Orchids of Britain*. Oxford University Press, Oxford.

Rich, M. D. B. & Rich, T. C.G., 1988, *Plant Crib*. B.S.B.I. Publications, Oundle.

Summerhayes, V. S., 1968, *Wild Orchids of Britain. 2nd Ed.* Collins New Naturalist, London.

REFERENCES

ANON, 1931, Observations. *Trans. Suffolk Nat. Soc.*, **1**, 224.

ANON, 1954, Proceedings. *Trans. Suffolk Nat. Soc.*, **9**, 62.

BATEMAN, R. M., 1981, The Hertfordshire *Orchidaceæ*. *Trans. Herts. Nat. Hist. Soc.* **28**, 56-79.

BATEMAN, R. M., 1985, Peloria and pseudopeloria in British orchids. *Watsonia*, **15**, 357-359.

BATEMAN, R. M. & Denholm, I. A., 1983, A reappraisal of the British and Irish dactylorchids, 1. The tetraploid marsh-orchids. *Watsonia*, **14**, 347-376.

BATEMAN, R. M. & Denholm, I. A., 1985, A reappraisal of the British and Irish dactylorchids, 2. The diploid marsh-orchids. *Watsonia*, **15**, 321-355.

BATEMAN, R. M. & Denholm, I. A., 1989, A reappraisal of the British and Irish dactylorchids, 3. The Spotted-orchids. *Watsonia*, **17**, 319-349.

BECKETT, C. *et al.*, 1987, *Suffolk Grassland Survey. The results of the Phase II/NVC Grassland Survey of Suffolk.* Suffolk Wildlife Trust, Saxmundham.

BELLAMY, D. J. & Rose, F., 1960, The Waveney-Ouse Valley Fens of the Suffolk-Norfolk Border. *Trans. Suffolk Nat. Soc.*, **11**, 367-385.

BOREHAM, H. J., 1962, Proceedings. *Trans. Suffolk Nat. Soc.*, **12**, 209.

BLOOMFIELD, E. N., 1858, Extracts from correspondence. *Phytologist, New Series* **2**, 557.

BULL, A. L., 1945, The Botany of Hitcham. *Trans. Suffolk Nat. Soc.*, **5**, 211.

BULL, A. L., 1977, A Century of Change. *Trans. Suffolk Nat. Soc.*, **17**, 220-224.

BURN, R., 1931, Species of plants new to Hind's Flora. *Trans. Suffolk Nat. Soc.*, **1**, 206-209.

BURTON, P. J., 1945, The Marsh Helleborine. *Trans. Suffolk Nat. Soc.*, **5**, 211.

COPPING, A., 1990, Plant records from Landguard Common 1985-88. *Trans. Suffolk Nat. Soc.*, **26**, 64-75.

COYTE, W. B., 1796, Hortus Botanicus Gippovicensis. privately published, Ipswich.

DAVIES, J. & P. & HUXLEY A., 1988, *Wild Orchids of Britain and Europe.* The Hogarth Press, London.

DICKINSON, P. G. M., 1949, Haverhill Plants. *Trans. Suffolk Nat. Soc.*, **7**, 10.

FARRELL, L., 1985, *Orchis militaris* L. Biological Flora of the British Isles. *J. Ecol.* **73**, 1041-1053.

FOLEY, M. J. Y., 1990a, The current distribution and abundance of *Orchis ustulata* L. in southern England. *Watsonia*, **18**, 37-48.

FOLEY, M. Y. J., 1990b, An assessment of populations of *Dactylorhiza traunsteineri* (Sauter) Soó in the British Isles and a comparison with others from Continental Europe. *Watsonia*, **18**, 153-172.

GALPIN, F. W., 1888, *An Account of the Flowering Plants of Harleston.* Bartlett & Co., London.

GARNETT, D. G., 1946, Orchideae near Leiston. *Trans. Suffolk Nat. Soc.*, **5**, 47.

GATHORNE-HARDY, R., 1959, *Iter Litorale, Trans. Suffolk Nat. Soc.*, **11**, 123-137.

GILLINGWATER, E., 1804, *Historical and descriptive account of St. Edmund's Bury.* Bury St. Edmunds.

GREEN, L., 1934, Records. *Botanical Exchange Club Report* **10**, 542.

GRIME, J. P., 1979, *Plant strategies and vegetation processes.* Wiley & Sons, Chichester.

HASLAM, S. M., 1965, The Breck Fens. *Trans. Suffolk Nat. Soc.*, **13**, 137-146.

HAWES, R., 1798, *History of Framlingham.* Woodbridge.

HEATHCOTE, G. D., 1986, The Lizard Orchid – A correction. *Trans. Suffolk Nat. Soc.*, **22**, 71.

HEATHCOTE, S. A., 1975, Observations on the Flora and origin of Redgrave and Lopham Fens. *Trans. Suffolk Nat. Soc.*, **17**, 46-48.

HENSLOW, J. S. & SKEPPER, E., 1860, *Flora of Suffolk.* Simpkin & Marshall, London.

HERMY, M. & VANHECKE, L., 1990, Orchids and nature management in Flanders: results of a mail questionnaire and a timely review of the situation. *Mém. Soc. Roy. Bot. Belg.*, **11**, 87-105.

HIND, W. M., 1889, *The Flora of Suffolk.* Gurney & Jackson, London.

HODGKINSON, J., 1783, *County of Suffolk surveyed.* London.

HYDE, E. M. & M. A. & SIMPSON, F. W., 1981, Some recent plant records. *Trans. Suffolk Nat. Soc.*, **18**, 233-241.

HYDE, E. M. & M. A. & SIMPSON, F. W., 1982, Some recent plant records. *Trans. Suffolk Nat. Soc.*, **18**, 298-303.

HYDE, E. M. & M. A. & SIMPSON, F. W., 1983, Some recent Suffolk plant records. *Trans. Suffolk Nat. Soc.*, **19**, 362-370.

HYDE, E. M. & SIMPSON, F. W., 1984, Some recent Suffolk plant records. *Trans. Suffolk Nat. Soc.*, **20**, 76-86.

HYDE, E. M. & SIMPSON, F. W., 1987, Some recent Suffolk plant records. *Trans. Suffolk Nat. Soc.*, **23**, 27-37.

JERMYN, S. T., 1974, *Flora of Essex.* Essex Naturalists' Trust, Fingringhoe.

LANG, D., 1980, *Orchids of Britain.* Oxford University Press, Oxford.

LETEN, M., 1990, Distribution dynamics of orchid species in Belgium: past and present distribution of thirteen species. *Mém. Soc. Roy. Bot. Belg.*, **11**, 133-155.

LITTLEWOOD, P. S., 1982, *Ancient Woodland in Mid-Suffolk.* M.Sc. Thesis, Unpublished.

MAYFIELD, A., 1911, Flora of a Suffolk Parish. *Journal of the Ipswich & District Field Club*, **3**, 18-28.

MENDEL, H., 1984, A tour round the vice-counties of Suffolk. *Trans. Suffolk Nat. Soc.*, **20**, 1-9.

MENDEL, H. & PIOTROWSKI, S. H., 1986, *The Butterflies of Suffolk.* Ipswich, Suffolk Naturalists' Society.

MILNE-REDHEAD, E., 1988, An uncommon hybrid orchid, *Dactylorhiza × transiens. Trans. Suffolk Nat. Soc.*, **24**, 82-83.

MITCHELL, N. S. P., 1955, Notes and observations. *Trans. Suffolk Nat. Soc.*, **9**, 270.

MORLEY, C., 1946, Suffolk Naturalists a century ago. *Trans. Suffolk Nat. Soc.*, **6**, 8-12.

MORLEY, R. A., 1933, Adventitious Bee-Orchids. *Trans. Suffolk Nat. Soc.*, **2**, 171.

PAGET, C. J. & J., 1834, *Sketch of the Natural History of Yarmouth.* Longman Rees, London.

PARKER, M., 1983, *Suffolk Trust for Nature Conservation Reserves Handbook, 6th Ed.* S.T.N.C., Saxmundham.

PERRING, F. H. & FARRELL, L., 1983, *British Red Data Books : 1. Vascular Plants. 2nd Edition.* R.S.N.C., Lincoln.

PERRING, F. H. & SELL, P. D., 1962, *Atlas of the British Flora.* B.S.B.I., T. Nelson & Sons, London.

PERRING, F. H., Sell, P. D. & Walters, S. M., 1964, *A Flora of Cambridgeshire.* Cambridge University Press, Cambridge.

PERRING, F. H. & SELL, P. D., 1968, *Critical Supplement of the Atlas of the British Flora.* B.S.B.I., T. Nelson & Sons, London.

PETCH, C. P. & SWANN, E. L., 1968, *Flora of Norfolk.* Jarrold, Norwich.

RACKHAM, O., 1980, *Ancient Woodland.* Arnold, Norwich.

RACKHAM, O., 1986, *The History of the Countryside.* Dent, London.

REINECKE, F., 1976, Über die Vermehrung von *Liparis læselii. Orchidee* **27**, 61-62.

RICH, T. C. G. & RICH, M. D. B., 1988, *Plant Crib.* B.S.B.I. Publications, Oundle.

ROBERTS, R. H., 1988, The occurrence of *Dactylorhiza traunsteineri* (Sauter) Soó in Britain and Ireland. *Watsonia* **17**, 43-47.

RONSE, A., 1989, In vitro propagation of orchids and nature conservation: possibilities and limitations. *Mém. Soc. Roy. Bot. Belg.*, **11**, 107-114.

ROWLING, E. S., 1956, Some interesting Suffolk wild flowers. *Trans. Suffolk Nat. Soc.*, **10**, 71-73.

RUSSELL-GEBBETT, J., 1977, *Henslow of Hitcham*. Terence Dalton Ltd, Lavenham.

RUTTERFORD, M. G., 1964, The coming of the 'Lizard Orchid' to the Breck. *Trans. Suffolk Nat. Soc.*, **13**, 24-25.

RUTTERFORD, M. G., 1975, Lizard Orchid at the Breck, further ten years. *Trans. Suffolk Nat. Soc.*, **17**, 69-70.

RUTTERFORD, M. G., 1985, The Lizard Orchid (*Himantoglossum hircinum*) at Lakenheath – a history of happenings since 1974. *Trans. Suffolk Nat. Soc.*, **21**, 50-51.

SANFORD, M. N., 1986, Mutant Green-winged Orchid. *Trans. Suffolk Nat. Soc.*, **22**, 74.

SANFORD, M. N., 1988, The Leopard Marsh Orchid. *Trans. Suffolk Nat. Soc.*, **24**, 80-81.

SIMPSON, F. W., 1935, The Flora of the County. *Trans. Suffolk Nat. Soc.*, **3**, 9-15.

SIMPSON, F. W., 1936, Remarkable plants of 1936. *Trans. Suffolk Nat. Soc.*, **3**, 180.

SIMPSON, F. W., 1937, The passing of chalk flowers. *Trans. Suffolk Nat. Soc.*, **3**, 276.

SIMPSON, F. W., 1940, Some plant records of 1940. *Trans. Suffolk Nat. Soc.*, **4**, 183.

SIMPSON, F. W., 1946, Botanical notes for 1946. *Trans. Suffolk Nat. Soc.*, **6**, 47-48.

SIMPSON, F. W., 1948, Wild flowers of 1948. *Trans. Suffolk Nat. Soc.*, **6**, 224-226.

SIMPSON, F. W., 1965, Flora of the coralline and red crags of East Suffolk. *Trans. Suffolk Nat. Soc.*, **13**, 7-10.

SIMPSON, F. W., 1982, *Simpson's Flora of Suffolk*. Suffolk Naturalists' Society, Ipswich.

SIMPSON, F. W., 1988, Additions and Corrections made by Rev. W. M. Hind to his Flora of Suffolk. *Trans. Suffolk Nat. Soc.*, **24**, 72-78.

SIMPSON, F. W., 1990, Past Distribution of the Burnt Orchid *Orchis ustulata* L. in Suffolk. *Trans. Suffolk Nat. Soc.*, **26**, 76-77.

STACE, C. A. (ed.), 1975, *Hybridisation and the Flora of the British Isles*. B.S.B.I./Academic Press, London.

SUMMERHAYES, V. S., 1968, *Wild Orchids of Britain*. 2nd Ed. Collins, New Naturalist, London.

S.W.T., 1989, *Reserves Handbook*. 7th Ed. Suffolk Wildlife Trust, Saxmundham.

TAYLOR, J. E., 1887, *Tourist's guide to the county of Suffolk*.

TRIST, P. J. O., 1956, Notes and observations. *Trans. Suffolk Nat. Soc.*, **10**, 80.

TRIST, P. J. O., 1960, An ecological study of *Fritillaria meleagris*. *Trans. Suffolk Nat. Soc.*, **11**, 392-399.

TRIST, P. J. O., 1979, *An Ecological Flora of Breckland*. B.S.B.I., E. P. Publishing Ltd, Norwich.

TUTIN, T. G. *et al.*, eds., 1964-1980, *Flora Europæa, 1-5*. Cambridge University Press, Cambridge.

WELLS, T. C. E., 1981, *Population ecology of terrestrial orchids*: p. 281-295 in: H. Synge (ed.) *The biological aspects of rare plant conservation*. Wiley & Sons, Chichester.

WILLIS, J. C. N., 1959, Some old records. *Trans. Suffolk Nat. Soc.*, **11**, 274-275.

WILLIS, J. C. N., 1960, Some Flora records of 1960. *Trans. Suffolk Nat. Soc.*, **11**, 390-392.

WILLIS, J. C. N., 1963, *Dactylorchis ericetorum*, Linton, and other orchids. *Trans. Suffolk Nat. Soc.*, **12**, 256-257.

YOUNG, A., 1813, *General view of the Agriculture of the County of Suffolk*. Sherwood, Neely and Jones, London.

ZINCKE, Rev. F. B., 1893, *Wherstead: some materials for its history*. 2nd Ed. Ipswich.

INDEX OF SPECIES